FRINTON -- JUL 2020

30-SECOND
NUMBERS

30-SECOND NUMBERS

The 50 key topics for
understanding numbers
and how we use them

Editors
Niamh Nic Daéid
Christian Cole

Contributors
Christian Cole
Niamh Nic Daéid
Raluca Eftimie
Harry Gray
Joyce Kafui Klu
John McDermott
David Pontin

Illustrations
Steve Rawlings

IVY PRESS

First published in the UK in 2020 by
Ivy Press
An imprint of The Quarto Group
The Old Brewery, 6 Blundell Street
London N7 9BH, United Kingdom
T (0)20 7700 6700
www.QuartoKnows.com

British Library Cataloguing-in-
Publication Data
A catalogue record for this
book is available from the
British Library.

ISBN: 978-1-78240-847-5

This book was conceived,
designed and produced by
Ivy Press
58 West Street
Brighton BN1 2RA, UK

Publisher David Breuer
Editorial Director Tom Kitch
Art Director James Lawrence
Commissioning Editor Kate Shanahan
Project Editor Joanna Bentley
Design Manager Anna Stevens
Designer Ginny Zeal
Picture Researcher Sharon Dortenzio
Illustrator Steve Rawlings
Glossaries Jane Roe

Printed in China

10 9 8 7 6 5 4 3 2 1

Dedication

It is not often in life that a slightly bonkers
conversation results in a beautiful, informative
and remarkable book. That conversation was
by email between Niamh Nic Daéid, Stephanie
Evans and Sue Black, the latter two pouring
equal measures of delight and scorn onto
Niamh's mad idea, from which **30-Second
Numbers** was born. This book, my fellow wise
owls, is dedicated to you both from wise owl
number two.

CONTENTS

INTRODUCTION
Niamh Nic Daéid, Eddie Small & Chris Cole

Numbers and marks to show them, such as ancient Egyptian hieroglyphics on the Karnak temple at Luxor, have been in use for thousands of years.

The use of numbers and tally marks to count and communicate is thought to be about 40,000 years old, possibly even older, charting the importance of the numerate human far back in our evolutionary history. In the modern era, numbers surround and pervade our very existence, forming the basis of almost every decision that we make every day of our lives.

In particular, the use of statistics and probabilities helps us make balanced decisions and underpin a rationale behind the choices we make, from health care to buying cars. We use numerical scales to decide how much we like our holiday destinations, how reliable some of our scientific evidence presented in a court room is, and how risky it is to have that extra glass of wine at the weekend or buy those shares on the stock market. Numbers communicate meanings and inferences about ourselves, our health and wellbeing, and about our world and how we interact with it. We are entering an era in our evolution where data and

Measuring aspects of our health helps in the provision of accurate and appropriate medical treatment.

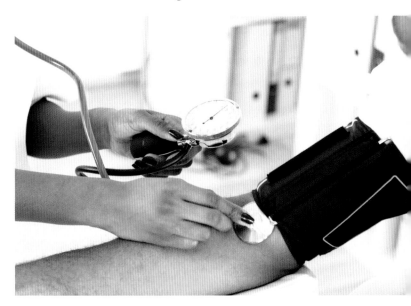

the analysis of incomprehensibly large datasets are being used to model and predict our behaviours in ways unimaginable to mathematicians of previous generations. A prime example of this is the advent of the Internet of Things and digital cities, where our phones, household appliances and other digital devices all become interconnected with each other, using numbers and code to communicate and monitor their environments so that your fridge can order your milk when you run out. The artificial intelligence and autonomous systems at the centre of these developments are all based on numerical code, mathematical tools and powerful algorithms. Numbers and how we use them really do matter.

However, notwithstanding this, many of us have a love-hate relationship with numbers and inwardly cringe when asked to help with the maths homework or undertake statistical tests as part of a project. In this book, we aim to set aside those fears by presenting each of 50 numbers and concepts underpinning the use of numbers in what we hope is a gentle, informative and engaging way.

The sums we learn at school are the foundations for a whole range of mathematical applications.

The text is laid out in six chapters. Each chapter begins with a glossary of terms and each includes a profile of one of our mathematical 'heroes', chosen by the different authors. Chapter four on probability, because we couldn't decide, gets two heroes. The first chapter, **Fundamental Numbers**, considers classifications of numbers you will remember from school, the basic building blocks of our understanding of what numbers are and how to tell the rational from the irrational. The second, **Statistical Distributions**, explores how numbers are used to explain different ways that data can behave, the types of variables that are used and how different tests can then be

With advances in artificial intelligence, more and more aspects of our lives can be controlled by digital technology.

undertaken to reveal trends and inferences within collected information. The third chapter, **Statistical Tests**, introduces some of the key concepts of statistics used in the many tests undertaken to explain connections between different variables and answers the question of 'what exactly is a p-value' that we were once asked by a senior legal colleague. Then follows **Probability and Risk**, exploring the causal relationship between two or more events from the basis of exploring the chance that they might occur. The importance of these concepts within the forensic science domain, in the understanding of the effects of new medical advancements and for environmental interventions is profound. Chapter six, **Using Numbers**, addresses how we may use numbers in real and tangible ways, exploring fractions, percentages, logarithms and algorithms. **Visualizing Numbers** is our final chapter, exploring the beauty revealed through the use of graphical representations of numerical data that have become essential tools in explaining and communicating trends and in comparing different datasets. Florence Nightingale, a pioneer in developing infographics, would be proud of what is achievable today. We finish with perhaps a look into the future addressing artificial intelligence, big data and machine learning.

Mathematics and statistics are beautiful, elegant and often mysterious languages, helping to unravel the secrets of the world around us. We truly hope that in this book we have helped provide some insights into their mysteries and revealed a window into their magic.

FUNDAMENTAL NUMBERS

FUNDAMENTAL NUMBERS
GLOSSARY

π Greek letter 'pi' representing a mathematical constant defined as the ratio of a circle's circumference to its diameter. It is approximately equal to 3.14159 and is an example of an irrational number.

$\sqrt{}$ Mathematical symbol for the square root. The square root of a number, x, is another number, y, with the property that $y \times y = x$.

Avogadro's number The number of molecules in a 'mole' of that chemical substance (usually atoms, molecules or ions), equal to $6.022140857 \times 10^{23}$.

binary digits In the binary numerical system there are only two digits: 1 and 0. This system is used by all computers and digital devices.

composite number A positive integer that is made by multiplying two smaller positive integers. A composite number cannot be a prime number.

conjugate A mathematical conjugate is when the sign is changed in a binomial, for example $x - y$ is the conjugate of $x + y$.

cryptography The mathematical study of methods used to encrypt and decrypt information ensuring its secure transmission.

denominator In a simple fraction (one number over another) the denominator is the bottom number and cannot be zero.

e A mathematical constant, also called Euler's number, which is approximately equal to 2.71828. It is the number whose natural logarithm is 1.

Fundamental Theorem of Arithmetic
Theory presented by ancient Greek mathematician Euclid in *Elements* c. 300 BCE. It states that every number greater than 1 is either a prime or is the product of primes.

imaginary number A non-real number that cannot be computed, called *i*; the square root of −1.

integer A whole number that can be positive or negative.

logarithm The opposite of an exponent. The resulting number raised by an exponent has the equivalent logarithm using the number as base and the exponent as the result: $8 = 2^3$ which is $\log_2 8 = 3$.

natural number Any positive integer.

numerator In a simple fraction the numerator is the top number.

polynomial An expression of at least two algebraic terms with different powers in a sum.

Sieve of Eratosthenes A simple method for finding all prime numbers up to a specified number, originally attributed to ancient Greek scholar Eratosthenes of Cyrene. Write all the integers to the number and then sequentially remove all numbers wholly divisible by 2, 3, 5, etc., which are greater than these numbers.

REAL NUMBERS

the 30-second calculation

3-SECOND COUNT

A real number is any value we can choose on the continuous number line, with the purpose of using it in real-world applications for measuring various quantities.

3-MINUTE TOTAL

Most constants in physical sciences (such as the gravity constant, or the speed of light constant), as well as physical variables (such as position, speed) are described using real numbers, as are most constants (such as Avogadro's number) and physiological variables (such as blood volume) in biological sciences and medicine.

René Descartes introduced the

term 'real number' in the seventeenth century, to distinguish between the real and imaginary solutions of polynomials (expressions formed of sums of several terms that contain different powers of the same variable; for example, $x^2 + 12x + 1 = 0$). In contrast to the natural numbers (numbers used in everyday life for counting, 0, 1, 2, 3, etc.) and integer numbers (the natural numbers together with their opposites, $-2, -1, 0, 1, 2$, etc.), the real numbers are difficult to define. They are basically any values on the continuous number line that can be used to measure quantities. Real numbers include natural numbers and integers, as well as numbers that contain decimal points. Thus the real numbers include and are classified in terms of both rational numbers (which can be written as a ratio of two integers) and irrational numbers (which cannot be written as a ratio of two integers). The real numbers form the largest set of numbers that we encounter in real-world applications. The fact that the sum, difference, multiplication and division (not by 0) of two real numbers give rise to another real number, allows us to use them to count, order and measure different quantities in everyday life: from buying groceries or calculating monthly mortgage payments to measuring the speed at which we drive our cars.

RELATED TOPICS

See also
RATIONAL NUMBERS
page 16

IRRATIONAL NUMBERS
page 18

3-SECOND BIOGRAPHY

RENÉ DESCARTES
1596–1650
French mathematician and philosopher who first used the term 'real' number, to distinguish it from an imaginary number in the context of solutions of polynomial equations

30-SECOND TEXT

Raluca Eftimie

Positive real numbers are used, for example, to describe distances, vehicle speeds and grocery costs.

RATIONAL NUMBERS

the 30-second calculation

3-SECOND COUNT
Rational numbers can be
expressed as the ratio of
two integers, a/b, where
a is called the numerator
while b is called the
denominator and must
be non-zero.

3-MINUTE TOTAL
Rational numbers have
numerous applications in
everyday life, from grocery
shopping (the cost of 1kg
of apples versus the cost
of a 0.5kg bag of apples),
to driving (measuring car
speeds) and cartography
(scales on maps to
represent distances
between places).

The term 'rational number'

comes from the fact that these numbers are
expressed as the 'ratio' of two integer numbers
(whole numbers that can be positive, negative
or zero; although one cannot divide by zero).
Since any integer a can be written as fractions
of the form $a/1$, it implies that all integers
are also rational numbers. The following types
of numbers are rational: whole numbers
(1.0; -22.0), numbers with exact decimals
(½ = 0.5), numbers with pure repeating decimals
(⅓ = 0.333333...). In contrast, those numbers
with non-repeating decimals are known as
irrational numbers. One of the earliest rigorous
studies of rational numbers is Euclid's *Elements*,
which deals (among other topics) with the ratios
of numbers. Rational numbers have various
properties that allow us to use them in everyday
life. For example, for any two rational numbers,
their sum, difference and product (as well as
division by a non-zero number) is also a rational
number (and therefore we can add/subtract/
multiply such numbers to measure things).
These simple properties can be used to show
another important property of rational numbers:
between any two such numbers there is always
another rational number. For example, if we
choose two rational numbers, p and q, it is clear
that $(p + q)/2$ is another rational number which
lies between p and q.

RELATED TOPICS
See also
PERCENTAGES
page 112

FRACTIONS
page 114

3-SECOND BIOGRAPHY
EUCLID
fl c. 300 BCE
Ancient Greek mathematician
(often referred to as the
founder of geometry) who
discussed rational numbers
in his work *Elements*

30-SECOND TEXT
Raluca Eftimie

*Positive rational
numbers can be used
to compare different
quantities when
shopping and cooking,
or to measure distances.*

IRRATIONAL NUMBERS

the 30-second calculation

3-SECOND COUNT
Irrational numbers are those numbers that cannot be expressed as the ratio of two integers, namely a/b, with a, b integers and b non-zero.

3-MINUTE TOTAL
Irrational numbers have various applications in engineering, architecture, physics, etc., being used, for example, to calculate the lengths and areas of various geometric objects, or to calculate angles between different trajectories in space.

Irrational numbers have been used and approximated since ancient times by mathematicians interested in astronomy and engineering. One of their first mentions comes from Hippasus of Metapontum, who discovered that the diagonal of a unit square (i.e. a diagonal of length $\sqrt{2}$) could not be expressed as the ratio of two whole numbers. In other words, $\sqrt{2}$ is not a rational number. More than two centuries later, Euclid gave a geometric proof of this result in his *Elements*. Nowadays, an irrational number is usually defined as a limit of a sequence of rational numbers, or defined by partitioning the rational numbers into subsets of numbers greater/less than the irrational number of interest. Examples of irrational numbers are $\pi = 3.141592654\ldots$, $\sqrt{2} = 1.414213562\ldots$, $e = 2.718281828\ldots$ In fact, all square roots of rational numbers (which are not perfect squares) are irrational numbers: e.g. $-\sqrt{5} = -2.2360679\ldots$ The main characteristic of irrational numbers is that they have non-repeating decimal expansions (see above the decimal expansions for π, e, $\sqrt{2}$, $-\sqrt{5}$). This aspect is mentioned by Stifel in his 1544 work *Aritmetica integra*, where he discussed the irrational numbers that could not be considered true numbers because they were 'concealed under a fog of infinity' (this 'fog' referring to the number of non-repeating decimals).

RELATED TOPICS
See also
REAL NUMBERS
page 14

RATIONAL NUMBERS
page 16

3-SECOND BIOGRAPHIES
KARL WEIERSTRASS
1815–97
German mathematician who presented the construction of irrational numbers in a series of lectures delivered in the 1860s in Berlin

RICHARD DEDEKIND
1831–1916
German mathematician who defined the rational and irrational numbers in his 1858 paper, 'Continuity and Irrational Numbers', where he also showed how these numbers combine to form real numbers

30-SECOND TEXT
Raluca Eftimie

Irrational numbers are used, for example, to calculate angles between different trajectories (using pi).

PRIME NUMBERS

the 30-second calculation

3-SECOND COUNT

A prime number is a natural number (greater than 1) that cannot be obtained by multiplying two strictly smaller natural numbers.

3-MINUTE TOTAL

As well as their importance in cryptography, prime numbers also appear in biology where, for example, some species of cicadas have life cycles of 13 years or 17 years, which gives them an evolutionary advantage.

A prime number p is a natural (discrete) number that has exactly two positive divisors: 1 and itself. Examples of prime numbers are 2, 3, 5, 7. In *Elements*, Euclid proved that there are infinitely many prime numbers. If a number p is not prime (i.e. p can be written as the product of two other numbers each strictly between 1 and p), then p is called a 'composite number'. The number '1' is neither prime nor composite. The prime numbers are the multiplicative building blocks of the natural numbers, meaning that each natural number can be written uniquely as the product of finitely many prime numbers, a result known as the Fundamental Theorem of Arithmetic. The fact that every number (no matter how large it is) can be factorized into primes, or the fact that two very large prime numbers can be multiplied to give rise to another number, has implications for computer security since it is very difficult to figure out quickly how an extremely large number can be decomposed into two prime numbers. This aspect is used in the encryption of messages, where in order to undo the encryption and read the message, one needs to know the prime numbers used for encryption.

RELATED TOPICS

See also
REAL NUMBERS
page 14

DISCRETE NUMBERS
page 24

3-SECOND BIOGRAPHY

ERATOSTHENES OF CYRENE
C. 276 BCE–C.194 BCE
Ancient Greek mathematician known as the founder of geography who proposed a simple method to calculate prime numbers

30-SECOND TEXT

Raluca Eftimie

Prime numbers are used in cryptography. They can also describe the life cycle of cicadas.

COMPLEX NUMBERS

the 30-second calculation

3-SECOND COUNT
Complex numbers are numbers which have been introduced to solve equations that involve square roots of negative real numbers.

3-MINUTE TOTAL
Due to Euler's identity $e^{ix} = \cos(x)+i\sin(x)$ (which holds for any real number x; where constant e is an irrational number defined as $e = 2.71828\ldots$), nowadays complex numbers are essential to describe phenomena that behave like a wave such as the alternating current, where both the current and the voltage vary in time like a sinusoidal wave.

Complex numbers are expressions of the form $a + ib$, where a and b are real numbers and i is a symbol defined as $i = \sqrt{(-1)}$. This symbol i is called the imaginary number (or the imaginary unit) and has the property that when it is squared it becomes a (negative) real number. The number a is called the real part of $a + ib$, while the number b is called the imaginary part of $a + ib$. For any complex number $a + ib$, the expression $a - ib$ is called its complex conjugate. The product of a complex number with its complex conjugate leads to real numbers (i.e. $(a + ib)(a - ib)=a^2 + b^2$). Even though the square root of a negative number was recorded around 50 CE when Heron of Alexandria studied the volume of a section of a pyramid, problems that involved square roots of negative numbers were deemed impossible to solve until the sixteenth century. The first major step was made in 1545 by Girolamo Cardano who, in his book *Ars Magna*, tried to solve the equation $x(10 - x) = 40$ and found two solutions: $x = 5 + \sqrt{(-15)}$ and $x = 5 - \sqrt{(-15)}$. René Descartes first introduced the term 'imaginary number' in 1637 in the context of solutions of polynomial equations. More than one century later, Leonhard Euler associated the symbol i with $\sqrt{(-1)}$. In the 1830s, Carl Friedrich Gauss introduced the term 'complex number' for an expression of the form $a + ib$.

RELATED TOPIC
See also
REAL NUMBERS
page 14

3-SECOND BIOGRAPHY
LEONHARD EULER
1707–83
Swiss mathematician who made important discoveries in many areas of mathematics and introduced various notations including the letter i to denote the imaginary number, and e to denote the base of the exponential function and the natural logarithm

30-SECOND TEXT
Raluca Eftimie

Complex numbers can describe physical phenomena that behave like waves.

DISCRETE NUMBERS

the 30-second calculation

RELATED TOPICS

See also
CONTINUOUS NUMBERS
page 26

NUMERICAL BASES
page 108

30-SECOND TEXT
David Pontin

3-SECOND COUNT

Discrete numbers are numbers taken from a set that contains only certain values, a typical example being the whole numbers 1, 2, 3, 4, etc.

3-MINUTE TOTAL

Discrete numbers form the basis for 'discrete mathematics'. They are used for counting, and as such form the basis for the most elementary ideas of quantity. Common examples are the integers, whole numbers (positive integers) or the bits (binary digits) in a binary number used in computing and digital communication, which may take the value either 0 or 1.

Discrete numbers can take only certain particular values, and these values cannot be meaningfully subdivided. One example would be the number of marbles in a jar. More formally, discrete numbers are either numbers taken from a finite set or numbers taken from an infinite set that is 'countable'. For this reason, discrete numbers are the first ones we meet when we start learning about mathematical concepts as children, since they can be used for counting. If we take the former (conceptually simpler) case first, a finite set is simply a set with a given finite number of entries, for example the whole numbers between 1 and 10. The numbers don't have to be whole, though; the set $\{1.1, 2.34, 5.987, 6\}$ is also a finite set. Discrete numbers can also come in infinite sets, the most familiar example being the whole numbers 1, 2, 3, 4, etc. The important thing is that for these numbers to be discrete the set should be 'countable'. This means that we can put the numbers in the set in order and match them up one-to-one with the whole numbers (even if this matching process goes on to infinity). Discrete numbers should be contrasted with continuous numbers, which cannot be counted because between any two numbers in a continuous set is another number.

Learning to count is one of the first things we do with numbers – in particular discrete numbers.

CONTINUOUS NUMBERS

the 30-second calculation

RELATED TOPIC
See also
DISCRETE NUMBERS
page 24

3-SECOND BIOGRAPHY
GEORG CANTOR
1845–1914
German mathematician who, in 1891, put forward his 'diagonal argument' which shows that the real numbers are not countable

3-SECOND COUNT
Continuous numbers are numbers that can take any value and are used to represent things that cannot be counted, but are instead measured, for example distance.

3-MINUTE TOTAL
To see that the real numbers are continuous, look for a number between 1 and 2. We can take, say, 1.1. We can also find a real number between 1 and 1.1, e.g. 1.01. Now, between 1 and 1.01 is 1.001, between 1 and 1.001 is 1.0001... And we could keep doing this forever.

Continuous numbers can be used to quantify concepts that can be subdivided in an infinite number of ways. Typical examples might be the weight of an apple, the temperature of the air at a point or the distance between two arbitrarily chosen points in space. Think of the latter example, and for concreteness take the distance between the points A and B. There is no restriction to the values that this distance can take, because we can move A any small or large amount closer to B, without restriction on how small or large the change in position of A. The most common example of a set of continuous numbers are the 'real numbers': these are the set of all positive and negative numbers. They can be represented by decimal numbers, where the number of decimal places can go on forever. Unlike discrete numbers, continuous numbers are not countable. We cannot even put them in order for the purpose of counting because between any two numbers in a continuous set is another number. Thinking of our representation using decimals, given any two decimal numbers we can always find a number between them by making use of extra decimal places after those in which the two numbers match in the decimal representation.

30-SECOND TEXT
David Pontin

Continuous numbers are used to represent things that can be measured, such as distance, weight or temperature.

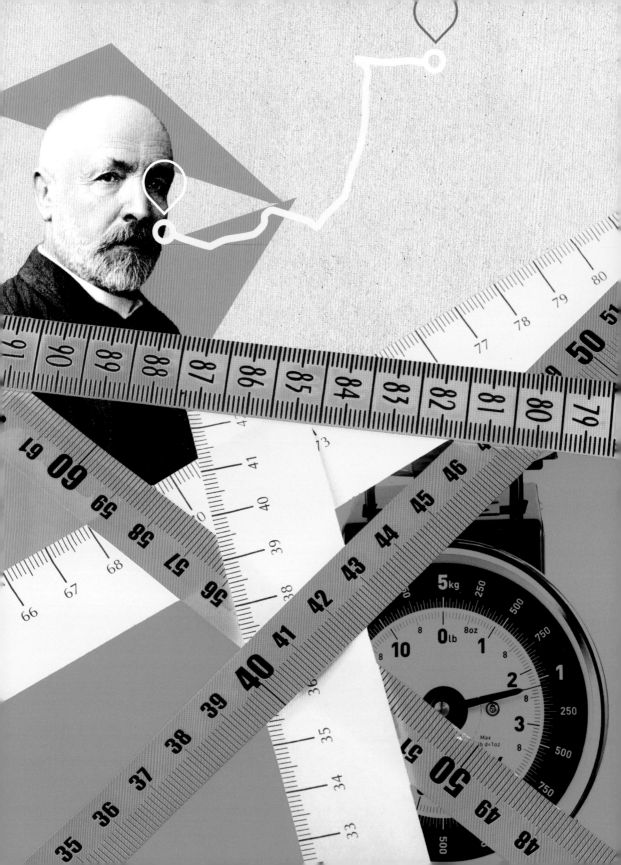

ZERO & NEGATIVE NUMBERS

the 30-second calculation

Numbers are often first

understood by counting objects, where zero and negative numbers are not used, but they facilitate more than counting. Zero represents the amount 'nothing' and is essential for writing numbers in the positional number system; for example, to distinguish between 301 and 31. Zero may also commonly represent a base point – such as the freezing point of water, or sea level in maps. In these settings, positive and negative numbers represent opposing directions away from the zero point. Basic arithmetic can be done using zero or negative numbers. Starting with any number and adding or subtracting 0 leaves the original number unchanged. Multiplying by 0 gives 0. However, division by 0 is undefined. Addition or subtraction with negative numbers may be thought of in terms of direction. To add -17 and $(+)12$ is equivalent to moving 17 steps in one direction, and then 12 in the opposite direction, ending up 5 steps in the first (negative) direction. Multiplication (or division) can be done by first ignoring any minus signs to obtain an answer, then adjusting by the rule that multiplying two numbers with the same sign gives a positive result, while multiplying a negative and a positive number together gives a negative result.

3-SECOND COUNT
Zero, or 0, represents nothing, no quantity or a base point on a scale. A negative number is a real number which is less than zero.

3-MINUTE TOTAL
Negative numbers and the number zero underpin fundamental arithmetic, and hence mathematics, but are also commonplace in everyday life. On a lift control panel, the ground floor is often labelled 0, while lower floors have negative numbers. In finance, negative numbers are widely used to denote debit amounts.

RELATED TOPICS
See also
REAL NUMBERS
page 14

POWERS & ROOTS
page 30

NUMERICAL BASES
page 108

3-SECOND BIOGRAPHY
BHASKARA II
1114–85
Indian mathematician who wrote about calculus hundreds of years before it was developed in Europe and analysed negative numbers in his *Crown of Treatises* (1150)

30-SECOND TEXT
John McDermott

Zero may represent freezing point or sea level, with negative numbers representing lower levels.

POWERS & ROOTS

the 30-second calculation

RELATED TOPICS

See also
ZERO & NEGATIVE NUMBERS
page 28

NUMERICAL BASES
page 108

LOGARITHMS
page 110

FRACTIONS
page 114

30-SECOND TEXT
John McDermott

3-SECOND COUNT
The second, third or higher power of a number is the result of multiplying two, three or more of that number together. Roots are the opposite of powers.

3-MINUTE TOTAL
Powers of numbers, or exponents as they are also known, grow really fast ('exponentially'). For example, while 3^7 is just over 2,000, 3^{12} is already over half a million. A 'googol' or 10^{100}, is massively more than the estimated number of atoms in the universe – a mere 10^{80}.

A power is the result of repeated multiplication of a number by itself. Three rows of three objects is nine. This is expressed as 'three squared is nine' or 'three to the power two is nine' and written mathematically as $3^2 = 9$, since there are two threes multiplied together. The superscript number is called the index. The term 'squared' is used because three rows of three forms a square. The first power of any number is just itself: $3^1 = 3$. The square root of a number is a second number which, multiplied by itself, gives the first. The square root of 9, often written as $\sqrt{9}$, is 3, and $\sqrt{25}$ is 5. The square root symbol $\sqrt{}$ can be adapted for higher roots by decoration with a small number, but is often replaced by fractional indices: $9^{1/2} = 3$ and $81^{1/4} = 3$. Powers of a number may be combined when multiplying: $3^7 = 3 \times 3 \times 3 \times 3 \times 3 \times 3 \times 3 = 3^4 \times 3^3$, for example, and $3^5 \times 3^2$, and so on, with the sum of the two indices always 7. Generally, two powers of a number multiplied together will give that number to the power of the sum of the two indices. The same power of two, possibly different, numbers may be combined: $2^2 \times 3^2 = 4 \times 9 = 36 = 6^2 = (2 \times 3)^2$. Negative indices represent fractions of 1 divided by that power, so that $3^{-4} = 1/3^4 = 1/81$. This is consistent for combining: $3^7 \times 3^{-4} = 3^{7+(-4)} = 3^3 = 27$.

We get a square number as the result when we multiply a number by itself.

24 September 1501
Born in Pavia in the
Duchy of Milan (now
part of Italy)

1518
Begins university studies
in Pavia, before
completing them in Padua

1526
Obtains doctorate in
medicine

1532
Moves to Milan

1534
Appointed lecturer in
mathematics at the Piatti
Foundation in Milan

1537
Publishes first two (of
many) mathematical
books, including *The
Practice of Arithmetic
and Simple Mensuration*

1543
Accepts the chair
of medicine at the
University of Pavia

1545
Publishes his most
celebrated work, *Artis
magnae sive de regulis
algebraicis liber unus*,
more commonly
called *Ars Magna*

1562
Appointed professor
of medicine at the
University of Bologna

1570
Jailed for heresy by the
Inquisition

1571
Released from jail, moves
to Rome

21 September 1576
Dies in Rome

GEROLAMO CARDANO

Gerolamo (or Girolamo) Cardano was an Italian polymath, who lived a colourful life and was a physician by trade. He studied medicine in Pavia, where he was born, and then in Padua, obtaining his doctorate in 1526. However, after leaving university he found it difficult to get employment due to his combative style and illegitimate birth, being repeatedly refused entry to the College of Physicians in Milan. There followed a period in which he practised medicine without a licence and also gambled heavily – this fascination with games of chance would later lead Cardano to lay the foundations for the theory of probability.

Eventually Cardano gained fame for the results of his medical practices and, with the help of influential backers, he was appointed to a mathematics teaching position at the Piatti Foundation in Milan in 1534. In 1537 he published his first two books on mathematics, and in his life ended up writing well over 100 books on mathematics, medicine, theology, astronomy and philosophy.

In 1545 Cardano's greatest work, *Ars Magna*, was published, in which he gave the solutions to cubic and quartic equations. In doing so he was the first person to work with imaginary numbers, in recognizing that the solution in some cases was obtained in terms of the square root of negative numbers. As with much of Cardano's life, however, the publication of *Ars Magna* was not without controversy. In 1539 Cardano had approached Niccolò Tartaglia to learn his method for solving particular types of cubics, and had reportedly sworn secrecy until Tartaglia himself published the work. Cardano considered himself released from his promise on later learning that the problem had in fact been previously solved by Scipione del Ferro, but a feud between Cardano and Tartaglia nevertheless ensued.

Cardano's passion for games of chance involving cards or dice would lead him to write in later life another highly influential book, *Liber de tudo aleae* (Book on Games of Chance), which was published posthumously. During a life in which he gambled heavily for long periods, he had determined that a scientific analysis of the games could allow determination of the most likely outcomes, and *Liber de tudo aleae* laid the foundation for the theory of probability and statistics.

David Pontin

STATISTICAL DISTRIBUTIONS

STATISTICAL DISTRIBUTIONS
GLOSSARY

σ The Greek letter sigma, which in statistics often represents the standard deviation of a population.

μ The Greek letter mu, which in statistics often represents the mean value of a set of data.

bell curve The colloquial name for a normal distribution, so named as it resembles the shape of a bell.

binomial distribution A discrete probability distribution of obtaining exactly n successes out of N trials.

census A nationwide analysis of the demographics of a country's population.

Chi-square distribution Also written as χ^2, a probability distribution with specific properties that can be used to test the 'goodness of fit' between an observed distribution and a theoretical one.

cluster A grouping of similar or related data points.

enumerators People who collect census data; in computing, it refers to processes for listing all elements in a set.

Gaussian distribution Another term for a normal distribution, named after German mathematician Carl Friedrich Gauss.

inferential statistics A branch of statistics that uses probability distributions to understand the properties of a population.

Poisson distribution The discrete distribution of counts of random events over a period of time with a constant rate.

population A set of similar items making up a collection selected as part of an experiment or census.

strata The Greek word for layers, a term sometimes used to describe clusters in a dataset.

Student's t-distribution A continuous distribution with a small sample size. It was developed by British statistician William Sealy Gosset under the pseudonym 'Student' as he wasn't allowed to use his own name by his employer, the Guinness brewery.

subpopulation A subset of a larger population, usually sharing a particular characteristic that is being studied.

uniform distribution A distribution with a constant probability. Also known as a rectangular distribution, reflecting its shape.

STATISTICS

the 30-second calculation

Statistics is a part of

mathematics that defines how data and information are collected from repetitive experiments. It involves the organization and analysis of data gathered, as well as using various tests to understand what the data means in the context of a particular question. Data is examined to determine the type of statistical model (or distribution) that may be applied and each model will have a set of associated statistical tests that can be carried out on the data. Experiments are designed to create a robust set of data and the samples that are generated should reflect the whole dataset (called a population) under study. Many repeat experiments are undertaken to generate a sample set of sufficient size. Statistical tests are used to test relationships between sets of data to see whether there are real differences between them or whether the differences observed are due to chance alone. This is called hypothesis testing. In order to apply the correct statistical tests the knowledge about the statistical distribution for the dataset is needed. This can sometimes be determined by simply graphing the data and observing any trends that suggest the shape of the resulting graph.

RELATED TOPICS

See also
SAMPLING
page 42

PROBABILITY
page 82

3-SECOND COUNT
Statistics is a general term used to describe an area of mathematics involving the collection, organization and analysis of data, normally from repetitive experimentation.

3-MINUTE TOTAL
Statistics are thought to have first been used back in the fifth century but developed more consistently from the mid-seventeenth century onwards. This era saw the generation and collections of tables of data related initially to population information and other measurable events such as temperature but also to data derived from experiments.

3-SECOND BIOGRAPHY
FLORENCE NIGHTINGALE
1820–1910
English social reformer who was the first female member of the Royal Statistical Society. She developed statistical graphs to show how hygiene improved health and to increase public understanding of data

30-SECOND TEXT
Niamh Nic Daéid

Graphing data allows an insight into trends and relationships that may be present.

POPULATION & SAMPLES

the 30-second calculation

RELATED TOPICS
See also
SAMPLING
page 42

BOOTSTRAPPING
page 72

3-SECOND COUNT
In statistics, population refers to all members, individuals or things in a defined group under study. A sample is a part or subset of the population under study.

3-MINUTE TOTAL
Population census is a process of collecting information; demographic, social and economic data about every individual living in a country (the whole population). A census is mostly conducted by governments over regular periods using enumerators to collect data from every home. The data collected is used for developmental, resource allocation, research and planning purposes. From a census data, sampling frames (source materials) are constructed from which samples are drawn for further studies.

Population is a statistical term referring to all the members of a defined group, for example the average weight of full-term babies born in the UK this year. The population will consist of all babies delivered from 37 weeks (full-term) in the UK. A population can be divided into subpopulations, which are subsets of a population with additional characteristics that may not be a representative of its population; for example, full-term *female* babies born in the UK. A sample, on the other hand, is a subset chosen to be representative of the population. Compared to subpopulation, a sample is not chosen to have additional characteristics but to mimic the characteristics of its population, so that estimates from a sample can be used to draw conclusions about an entire population. Instead of collecting data on every single full-term baby, for instance, a small subset of babies can be randomly sampled across the country to represent the population. It's sometimes necessary to model subpopulations separately and combine their effects if distinct characteristics exist between subgroups; for example, if male babies are known to be heavier than females. Ideally, complete population data would be collected, but this is practically impossible, so researchers rely on samples to draw inferences about the whole population.

3-SECOND BIOGRAPHY
ALEXANDER IVANOVICH CHUPROV
1841–1908
Russian professor of political economy and statistics who introduced sample survey to Imperial Russia in the early 1870s by interviewing about 4.5 million Russian muzhiks with the hope to provide a statistical description of the Russian peasant community

30-SECOND TEXT
Joyce Kafui Klu

To draw meaningful conclusions about a population using a sample, the sample must exhibit the characteristics of the population and be of good size.

SAMPLING

the 30-second calculation

Sampling is a statistical technique of picking out a subset of items from a population of items, which here could mean anything including people, animals and objects. Sampling is useful in situations where accessing a whole population is practically impossible, costly and/or time demanding. The idea of sampling is to use information on a subset of items to draw conclusions about the whole population of interest. For example, to determine if a pot of soup has the right amount of salt, you will take a spoonful (a sample) to draw conclusions about the level of salt in the whole pot (population). Sampling can be done at random or by an organized approach. For instance, to interview a number of individuals from a community telephone directory, sampling can be done by randomly choosing the required telephone numbers from the whole list (random sampling); by selecting every tenth telephone number (systematic sampling); by grouping the telephone numbers by areas within the community (strata) and sampling from each area (stratified sampling); or by dividing the list of telephone numbers into a number of groups (clusters) and sampling those (cluster sampling).

3-SECOND COUNT
Sampling is the process of selecting a small number of items from a larger population.

3-MINUTE TOTAL
Sampling is employed in many fields. In manufacturing and quality control especially, it is practically impossible to examine every item in a production batch for quality assessment. In most cases, a small fraction of items is sampled and examined in order to draw conclusions about the quality of a whole production batch.

RELATED TOPICS
See also
POPULATION & SAMPLES
page 40

BOOTSTRAPPING
page 72

3-SECOND BIOGRAPHY
PIERRE-SIMON LAPLACE
1749–1827
French scholar who made significant contributions to the fields of mathematics, statistics, physics and astronomy. Using a sample, he estimated the population of France in 1786

30-SECOND TEXT
Joyce Kafui Klu

Sampling at random avoids bias by giving each item in the population an equal chance of being selected.

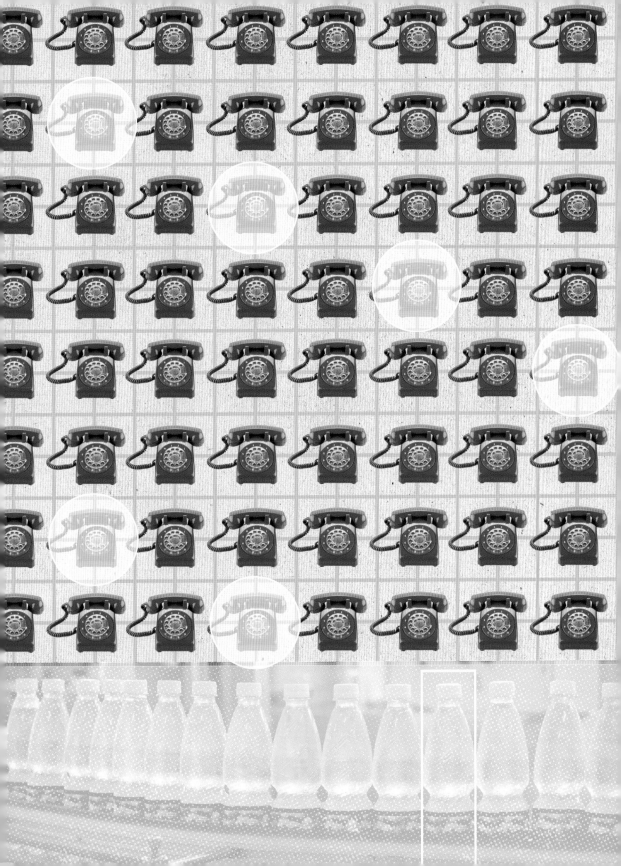

INDEPENDENT & DEPENDENT VARIABLES

the 30-second calculation

3-SECOND COUNT
The independent variables are those variables that are manipulated in experiments and their effects are measured, while the dependent variables are those that depend on the independent variables.

3-MINUTE TOTAL
Any scientific experiment involves these two key variables. For example, the number of cigarettes smoked (an independent variable) can be investigated in terms of its effects on the incidence of lung cancer (a dependent variable). Or the weather (an independent variable) can be investigated in terms of its effects on the monthly high street sales (a dependent variable).

A variable describes something

that we want to measure (from objects, to events, behaviours and even feelings). The independent variable is one that is manipulated in experiments, while the dependent variable measures the effect of the independent variables. In an experiment, it is very important to decide which variables are the independent ones (proposing the cause), and which are the dependent ones (measuring the effects). Such a decision is not always easy, and it ultimately depends on the questions being investigated in the experiments. For example, asking the question 'Do people with a healthy diet tend to exercise more?' suggests that the diet could be considered the independent variable while the exercise is the dependent one. However, asking 'Do people who exercise more tend to have a healthy diet?' suggests that the exercise could be the independent variable while the diet could be considered the dependent one. When sketching the correlation between these variables, we usually represent the dependent variable on the vertical (y) axis, and the independent variable on the horizontal (x) axis. Therefore, we can think about these variables in terms of functions: the independent variable (y) could be seen as a function of the dependent variable (x): $y = f(x)$.

RELATED TOPIC
See also
RANDOM VARIABLES
page 52

3-SECOND BIOGRAPHY
ANDREY KOLMOGOROV
1903–87
Russian mathematician who formulated, in his 1933 book *Foundations of the Theory of Probability*, a set of axioms that form the foundations of probability theory. The book introduced in an abstract way the concept of random variables

30-SECOND TEXT
Raluca Eftimie

Real-life dependent and independent variables: plants depend on water to grow, good health depends on fruits and vegetables.

STATISTICAL DISTRIBUTIONS

the 30-second calculation

The distribution is a function

that describes the probability of occurrence of an experiment outcome, which is given numerically by a random variable. Based on the two types of random variables, namely discrete (which can take a finite number of values) and continuous (which can take any value on an interval), there are two types of distributions: discrete and continuous. Discrete distributions include the binomial distribution (which gives the probability of successes in n independent trials that can have only two outcomes: 'success' and 'failure'), and the Poisson distribution (which describes the probability to find exact r events in a given length of time if the events occur independently at a constant rate μ). Continuous distributions include normal distribution (the most important of all distributions, as it describes a large variety of events that occur by chance when large numbers of random samples are taken), the Student's t-distribution (used for small numbers of random samples), exponential distribution (used to model the interval between two occurrences), the Chi-square distribution (used in inferential statistics for hypothesis testing), and the uniform distribution (used for both discrete and continuous data where the outcomes have equal probabilities of occurrence).

3-SECOND COUNT
A statistical (or probability) distribution describes how likely certain outcomes in experiments are.

3-MINUTE TOTAL
Most data can be described by one of the distributions discussed here, and thus there are numerous applications of these distributions: from the use of Poisson distribution to characterize traffic flow or the particle counts during radioactive decay, to using normal distribution to approximate people's IQs.

RELATED TOPICS
See also
RANDOM VARIABLES
page 52

PROBABILITY
page 82

30-SECOND TEXT
Raluca Eftimie

Statistical distributions can describe various physical phenomena, such as particle counts during radioactive decay.

NORMAL DISTRIBUTION

the 30-second calculation

The normal distribution is one
of the most used distributions in statistics.
Abraham de Moivre first described it at the
beginning of the eighteenth century, in the
context of laws of change that could govern
gambling, and subsequently Marquis de Laplace
and Carl Friedrich Gauss described the classical
normal distribution in the context of errors for
astronomical data. The name 'normal' was the
result of an incorrect perception of nineteenth-
century scientists who thought that this
distribution described the natural pattern of
distributions, and anything that deviated from
it should be investigated. If one knows the
mean (μ) and the variance (σ^2) (or the standard
deviation σ) of a set of measurements (x), then
the probability distribution that characterizes
this knowledge is the normal distribution, which
is described by the following formula:

$$\frac{1}{\sigma\sqrt{2\pi}}\, e^{-(x-\mu)^2/2\sigma^2}$$

The value of the mean (μ) fixes the location of
this normal curve on the measurement space,
while the variance describes the spread of the
measurements. Moreover, this formula tells us
that the observations (i.e. measurements)
around the mean μ are more likely to occur than
observations further away from the mean.

3-SECOND COUNT
A normal distribution is
a symmetric distribution
that has the shape of a bell
curve. It is considered one
of the most important
distributions in statistics.

3-MINUTE TOTAL
The importance of normal
distribution in real life and
its applicability to so many
problems stems from a
mathematical result (called
the Central Limit Theorem),
which says that if we take
sufficiently large random
samples from a population
with mean μ and variance
σ^2 then the sample means
will be approximated by a
normal distribution.

RELATED TOPIC
See also
STATISTICAL DISTRIBUTIONS
page 46

3-SECOND BIOGRAPHIES
ABRAHAM DE MOIVRE
1667–1754
French mathematician known
for de Moivre's formula, which
connects complex numbers and
trigonometry, and for his work
on normal distributions

CARL FRIEDRICH GAUSS
1777–1855
German mathematician who
made contributions to many
mathematical fields, including
astronomy, where he used
normally distributed
measurement errors to predict
the position of the dwarf
planet Ceres

30-SECOND TEXT
Raluca Eftimie

*Normal distribution
can be used to describe
the odds of winning
games of chance,
such as card games.*

26 May 1667
Born in Vitry-le-François, France

1678
Studies at the Protestant Academy in Sedan, France

1682
Studies at the Protestant Academy in Saumur, France

1684
Studies physics at the Collège de Harcourt, in Paris

1687
Admitted to the Savoy Church in London (the exact date de Moivre moved to England is not known)

1697
Elected fellow of the Royal Society

1706
Becomes an English citizen

1718
Publishes *The Doctrine of Chances*, the first book on probability theory

1725
Publishes *Annuities upon Lives*, in which he uses mortality statistics to formulate the theory of annuities

1730
Publishes *Miscellanea Analytica*, a compendium of his mathematical results

1754
Admitted to the Royal Academy of Sciences in Paris

27 November 1754
Dies in London, at the age of 87

ABRAHAM DE MOIVRE

Abraham de Moivre was born in 1667 in France and attended school from an early age. In addition to formal studies in Latin and Greek (at Catholic and Protestant schools), he learned arithmetic with the help of a tutor as well as through his own readings. He further studied, on his own, various mathematical texts on games of chance and geometry. His first formal mathematical training was received at the age of 17, when he took physics courses at the Collège de Harcourt in Paris.

Following the religious prosecution of Protestants in France (which started in 1685), de Moivre moved to England, where he continued to read mathematical books on his own (such as Newton's *Principia Mathematica*), while tutoring students at the same time.

De Moivre was poor throughout his life. As well as tutoring he was a regular customer of Slaughter's Coffee House in London (which was also a favourite meeting place of French immigrants and of chess players), where gamblers paid him for his advice on winning chances. He sought professorial positions at Dutch and English universities but was always refused. Nevertheless, de Moivre wrote numerous books and articles.

From a scientific point of view, de Moivre is known for his pioneering work on probability theory. His book *The Doctrine of Chances* contains the definition of statistical independence, as well as the approximation of the binomial distribution by the normal distribution. This book also shows calculations of constant values describing standard deviations. He is also known for a formula that now bears his name ($e^{nix} = cos(nx) + i\ sin(nx) = (cos\ x + i\ sin\ x)n$), which connects complex numbers and trigonometric functions.

De Moivre is famed for allegedly predicting his own death. It is said that he observed that he had started sleeping longer and longer every night, and predicted that he would die the day when his extra minutes of sleep would accumulate to 24 hours. The predicted date was 27 November 1754, the actual date of his death.

Raluca Eftimie

RANDOM VARIABLES

the 30-second calculation

A random variable's value might depend on the outcome of a 'random' process (for example, tossing a coin), or the possible results of an experiment which is either yet to be performed, or where the outcome is a measurement in which some error is involved. These random variables can have a value within some interval, or in other words, between some maximum and minimum values. These maximum and minimum values could be finite or infinite. A continuous random variable may take any value within the interval (its value is taken from a set of continuous numbers like the real numbers). Such a random variable typically arises from a measurement of length, temperature, weight, etc. By contrast, discrete random variables may take values from a set of discrete numbers. In other words, they may only take certain values within the interval (and the number of these possible values is countable) – returning to the example of tossing a coin, say, 20 times, the number of heads obtained is a whole number between 1 and 20. Statistical theories and techniques are developed separately for analysing the properties of sets of either discrete or continuous random variables. The two are, however, closely related.

3-SECOND COUNT
A random variable is one whose value depends on chance. For a discrete random variable this value is taken from a set of discrete numbers. Discrete and continuous random variables differ by the possible values that they may take.

3-MINUTE TOTAL
One example of a random variable would be the number obtained when a die is rolled. In this case the limits of the interval are 1 and 6, and the allowed values of the random variable are 1, 2, 3, 4, 5 and 6 only, making this a discrete random variable.

RELATED TOPICS
See also
DISCRETE NUMBERS
page 24

CONTINUOUS NUMBERS
page 26

3-SECOND BIOGRAPHY
GEROLAMO CARDANO
1501–76
Italian mathematician, one of the first people to try to analyse the outcomes of games of chance, described by random variables. This led to the foundation of probability theory

30-SECOND TEXT
David Pontin

The outcomes of games of chance – such as rolling a die or tossing a coin – are random variables.

STATISTICAL TESTS

σ The Greek letter sigma, which in statistics often represents the standard deviation of a population.

$\sqrt{}$ Mathematical symbol for the square root. The square root of a number, x, is another number, y, with the property that $y \times y = x$.

ANOVA test ANalysis Of VAriance test used to examine statistical differences between two groups.

Chi-square distribution Also written as χ^2, a probability distribution with specific properties that can be used to test the 'goodness of fit' between an observed distribution and a theoretical one.

median The middle value in an ordered set of numbers.

mode The most common value in a set of numbers.

null hypothesis The default assumption of an experiment that there is no relationship between the variables under observation.

observation error A technical error introduced during measurements of quantities or values.

plausible values A range limit within which the real value is likely to be found.

point estimate A single or exact value for an unknown parameter.

reproducibility crisis A recent phenomenon in several scientific fields where attempts to reproduce many published studies have not been possible, leading to concerns of lack of rigour in publications and/or methodology.

scatter graph A plot of two continuous variables on x and y axes.

significance level The threshold defined where a statistical p-value is considered 'significant'. Often set as 0.05.

t-test A pairwise test of two normally distributed datasets under the assumption that they are from the same distribution.

variance A measure of the variability in a sample or distribution. Also, the square of the standard deviation.

STATISTICAL TESTS

the 30-second calculation

Statistical tests evaluate

quantitatively the strength of evidence for a claim. The purpose of a statistical test is to ascertain whether there is enough evidence to reject or fail to reject a given claim. For example, a statistical test can be used to evaluate the claim that school A outperforms school B. The claim to be tested is called the hypothesis, which is subdivided into null and alternative hypotheses. A null hypothesis, denoted with H_0, is a claim of equality (no difference) between variables being tested. By default, the null hypothesis is considered to be true unless there is enough evidence to prove otherwise. An alternative hypothesis, denoted with H_1, is a statement of inequality (difference) between the variables being tested. For example, H_0 claims that school A performs the same as school B; H_1 claims that school A outperforms school B. A statistical test will test the claim H_0 against H_1 by computing a probability value called p-value. The null hypothesis is rejected if the p-value is below a particular threshold (see page 66) and it is accepted otherwise. Failing to reject H_0 implies that there is enough evidence from data to support the claim of equality (no difference) between the variables being tested.

RELATED TOPICS
See also
P-VALUES
page 66

CONFIDENCE INTERVAL
page 70

HYPOTHESIS TESTING
page 88

3-SECOND BIOGRAPHY
JOHN ARBUTHNOT
1667–1735
Scottish physician who was the first to use statistical tests to investigate human sex ratio at birth using 82 years of birth records in London

30-SECOND TEXT
Joyce Kafui Klu

3-SECOND COUNT
A statistical test is a way to investigate if evidence from data is strong enough to support a given hypothesis.

3-MINUTE TOTAL
Depending on the specific questions of interest, there are different methods including T-test, ANOVA and Chi-square test for performing statistical tests. T-test is used to test the equality of two population means; for more than two populations, ANOVA test is used. Chi-square test compares categorical variables, testing for variable association or fitness of model.

Failing to reject a null hypothesis doesn't mean that it is accepted as truth, only that there is enough evidence to support it.

MEAN

the 30-second calculation

Mean, also called average, is a central representation of data. Using mean is most convenient when reporting large datasets that need to be summarized with a single value. For example, at the end of a week, a doctor reporting on the total number of patients treated on a daily basis will need to report the mean, mainly because the number of patients treated each day will vary over the week. A teacher can summarize the performance of a class using the mean. Mean is computed by dividing the sum of all values by the number of values summed. Mean computed using this approach is termed arithmetic mean and is the most commonly used. For example, if the number of patients treated in a week are {3,5,7,2,4,3}, then on average four patients ([3 + 5 + 7 + 2 + 4 + 3]/6 = 4) are treated daily. In situations where taking arithmetic mean is not applicable, other types of mean, including geometric and harmonic, can be used. Geometric mean is used when comparing things with very different properties. Harmonic mean is used for finding the mean involving rates or ratios. Mean computed with all population data is termed population mean and mean from sample data is termed sample mean.

3-SECOND COUNT
Mean is a statistical term referring to a single value that describes a set of data by identifying the midpoint position of the data.

3-MINUTE TOTAL
Mean, median and mode are the three main but different statistical approaches for determining the central position of data. Median is a middle value that divides data into two equal halves – the median of {2,3,5,7,8} is 5. Mode is the most occurring value in data – the mode of {1,3,3,7,9} is 3. Where a few of the data values are extremely small or large (termed outliers), median is preferred over mean as mean is influenced by outliers.

RELATED TOPICS
See also
POPULATION & SAMPLES
page 40

SAMPLING
page 42

STANDARD DEVIATION
page 62

3-SECOND BIOGRAPHY
JAMES BRADLEY
1693–1762
English astronomer who used mean to describe his test of observations leading to the discovery of the aberration of light

30-SECOND TEXT
Joyce Kafui Klu

In most cases the population mean is estimated using sample mean because obtaining full population data can be impossible.

$$\frac{3 + 5 + 7 + 2 + 4 + 3}{6} = 4$$

STANDARD DEVIATION

the 30-second calculation

3-SECOND COUNT
Standard deviation is a statistical measure of how variable or spread a set of data is about the mean.

3-MINUTE TOTAL
To obtain the exact range of an unknown parameter, the standard deviation is used to compute a confidence interval; an interval with an associated probability of confidence. This is particularly useful for daily investment decision making. Given different investment options, standard deviation measures the associated risk or volatility of each option for deciding on the best available option.

Standard deviation measures how each value in a set of data deviates from the mean. Low standard deviation indicates that data values are close to the mean and high standard deviation indicates that data is widely spread. For example, a stock that pays an average of 5% with a standard deviation of 2% implies that one could earn around 3% $(5 - 2)$ to 7% $(5 + 2)$. Suppose the standard deviation is 12% instead, then one could make a loss of about 7% $(5 - 12 = -7)$ or a profit of about 17% $(5 + 12)$. Standard deviation is calculated as the square root of the variance or average squared deviation from the mean. Suppose the test scores of a class are $[63, 70, 55, 82, 59]$. The standard deviation can be computed in the following three steps. First, find the mean using $[63 + 70 + 55 + 82 + 59]/5 = 65.8$. Second, find the variance using $[(63 - 65.8)^2 + (70 - 65.8)^2 + (55 - 65.8)^2 + (82 - 65.8)^2 + (59 - 65.8)^2]/(5 - 1) = 450.8/5 = 112.7$. Finally, take the square root of variance as $\sqrt{(112.7)} = 10.6$. Assuming the only available information is a mean score of 65.8 and a standard deviation of 10.6, one can tell that the performance of the class ranges between 55.2 $(65.8 - 10.6)$ and 76.4 $(65.8 + 10.6)$. Knowing the standard deviation associated with the mean of a data gives a better picture of how variable the data is and can be useful in decision making.

RELATED TOPICS
See also
MEAN
page 60

CONFIDENCE INTERVAL
page 70

RANGES
page 144

30-SECOND TEXT
Joyce Kafui Klu

Standard deviation tells how representative a reported mean is of a set of data.

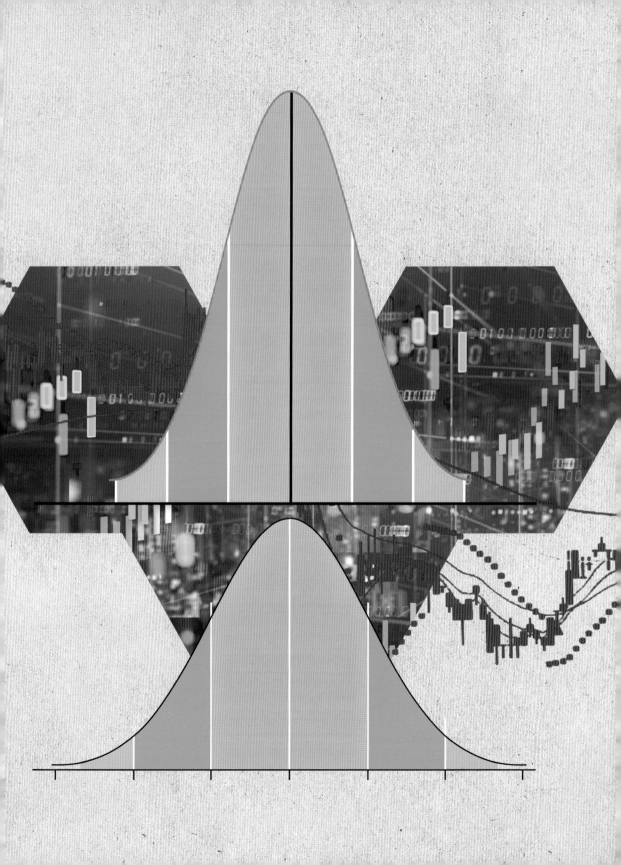

MEASUREMENT ERROR

the 30-second calculation

RELATED TOPICS
See also
STANDARD DEVIATION
page 62

CONFIDENCE INTERVAL
page 70

3-SECOND COUNT
Measurement error is the difference between the value of a measured quantity and its true value.

3-MINUTE TOTAL
The estimation of measurement error (uncertainty) is an increasing requirement for testing laboratories to meet accreditation standards across the globe. The police and juries rely heavily on laboratories to estimate the amount of illegal substances in a person's urine or blood. When the measured value of an illegal substance is obtained, an estimate of measurement uncertainty is subtracted from the measured quantity to account for possible error from instruments and method used.

Measurement error, also known as observation error, is the error associated with a measured value when compared with its true value. For example, a thermometer may give a temperature reading of 9°C when the true temperature is in fact 8°C. Measurement error can be random or systematic. Random errors occur naturally due to fluctuations in the readings of instruments. These errors cannot be controlled or avoided; as a result, a measurement repeated under the same conditions will produce different results. The effect of random errors can be reduced by taking repeated measurements and averaging the results. Systematic error, on the other hand, occurs due to the inaccuracies of instruments or incorrectly calibrated instruments and introduces a constant or predictable error to the true value, which affects all measurement. When systematic error is present, a measurement repeated under the same conditions will produce the same result. This makes systematic errors difficult to detect but, if the source of the error can be identified, easy to rectify. Systematic and random error account for the total error associated with a measurement. It may be impossible to avoid errors completely, especially random ones. However, taking careful steps to reduce errors in measurement is particularly important if results are to be trusted and relied upon.

3-SECOND BIOGRAPHY
WILLIAM GEMMELL COCHRAN
1909–80
Scottish-American statistician and author of early text books on measurement or observation error and experimental designs

30-SECOND TEXT
Joyce Kafui Klu

In statistics, error is not considered a mistake but a deviation in measurements that could be inevitable even under correct experimental settings.

P-VALUES

the 30-second calculation

Many experiments revolve

around case-control studies where two groups are tested: one is the 'control' and the other the 'case'. The control group is subjected to 'normal' but controlled conditions, such as a constant temperature, whereas the case group is subjected to different temperatures. The response, such as plant growth, is measured. The average effect of the case group is compared to the control in what's called the null hypothesis (H_0) significance test (NHST). A statistical test (see page 58) allows us to determine whether the difference between conditions is significant or not. The statistical test calculates a p-value, which is the probability that the data is equal to or more extreme than its observed value. A p-value, like all probabilities, is between 0 and 1, with 1 meaning a near certainty and 0 a near impossibility. Thus, if the statistical test results in a value close to 0 then it is improbable that the observed effect is due to random chance and H_0 can be rejected. In 1925 the statistician Ronald Fisher suggested that if $p < 0.05$, the result was statistically significant. Since then, this suggestion has become a rule, with the p-value being misinterpreted and over trusted. A purely statistically significant result does not reflect on the size of the effect, nor on its generalizability. Importantly, it does not guarantee the controlled variable is causal of the result.

3-SECOND COUNT
Calculate a p-value to check whether the results from an experiment are statistically significant.

3-MINUTE TOTAL
P-values are a useful aid for deciding whether a result is worthy of further investigation. Their overuse in the scientific literature, however, has controversially been implicated in a 'reproducibility crisis', with senior statisticians (such as the American Statistical Association) giving guidance on how to use statistical tests effectively.

RELATED TOPICS
See also
PROBABILITY
page 82

HYPOTHESIS TESTING
page 88

3-SECOND BIOGRAPHY
SIR RONALD AYLMER FISHER
1890–1962
Pioneering British statistician and geneticist whose work on randomness and variance had a huge impact on efficient farming practices

30-SECOND TEXT
Christian Cole

Scientific experiments control variables and measure outcomes multiple times in order to calculate statistical significance via p-values.

11 August 1895
Born in Hampstead,
London

1920
Earns a BA in
Mathematics from Trinity
College, Cambridge

1921
Appointed lecturer at the
Department of Applied
Statistics, University
College London

1924
Becomes assistant editor
of the journal *Biometrika*

1933
Promoted to Readership,
Department of Applied
Statistics, University
College London

1933
Elected head of the
Department of Applied
Statistics, University
College London

1935
Promoted to
professorship,
Department of Applied
Statistics, University
College London

1935
Awarded the Weldon
Prize

1936
Becomes managing editor
of *Biometrika*

1946
Awarded the Commander
of the Most Excellent
Order of the British
Empire (CBE)

1955
Awarded the Guy Gold
Medal

1955
Elected president of the
Royal Statistical Society

1966
Elected fellow of the
Royal Society

12 June 1980
Dies at Midhurst, England

EGON PEARSON

Egon Sharpe Pearson was born in London to Maria Sharpe and Karl Pearson, a renowned mathematician and biostatistician known for developing major statistical techniques widely in use today, including correlation and regression coefficients, Chi-squared test, p-value and method of moments.

Like father like son, Egon Pearson attended Dragon School, Oxford and Winchester College, after which he gained admission to read mathematics at Trinity College, Cambridge in 1914. World War I interrupted his studies at Cambridge but after the war the Military Special Examination was set up to help those whose studies had been disrupted by the war. Egon Pearson took this examination, after which he was awarded a Bachelor's degree at Trinity College, Cambridge.

He took up a lectureship position at his father's Department of Applied Statistics at University College London. Although appointed as a lecturer, his father wouldn't give him the opportunity to lecture; instead, Egon attended his father's lectures. Around this time, he began to produce high quality research work on statistics and become an assistant editor of *Biometrika*, a statistical journal co-founded by his father. His research work contributed significantly to the field of statistics. He later become the head of department after his father resigned due to ill health.

Egon Pearson is famous for developing, along with Jerzy Neyman, the Neyman-Pearson theory of testing statistical hypotheses, which served as the basis for the modern theory of hypothesis testing. Throughout his career, he developed several statistical methodologies and advances in the use of the likelihood ratio for statistical inference. He also pioneered the application of statistical methods to other fields, including industrial standardization and quality control, agricultural research and the assessment and testing of weapons during and after World War II.

Pearson received several honours for his impactful contributions to modern statistics. Although not a public figure, his sustained contribution to publication, teaching and supervision was recognized in honours including the CBE, Guy Medal in Gold, Presidency of the Royal Statistical Society and Fellowship of the Royal Society.

Joyce Kafui Klu

CONFIDENCE INTERVAL

the 30-second calculation

Confidence interval uses a sample data to compute a range of values that may contain the true value of an unknown population parameter of interest at a specified percentage probability. A probability of 90%, 95% or 99% is commonly used in practice. A 95% confidence interval means that if numerous samples are drawn from the same population and confidence interval is computed, then the resulting confidence interval will surface 95% of the cases to include the true population parameter. Confidence interval can be contrasted with point estimate, which computes a single or an exact value for the unknown parameter. The idea of confidence interval is to understand the variability associated with an estimated parameter and to enhance its reliability by computing a range of plausible values (rather than a single value) believed to contain the true value of the unknown parameter. The width of a confidence interval is influenced by the specified percentage probability, the size of the sample taken and the variability of data. A high percentage probability will broaden the estimated confidence interval. The higher the variability in data, the wider the estimated confidence interval. With a large sample size, a good estimate of the unknown population parameter with a narrow confidence interval can be achieved.

RELATED TOPICS
See also
ZERO & NEGATIVE NUMBERS
page 28

STATISTICAL DISTRIBUTIONS
page 46

MEAN
page 60

STANDARD DEVIATION
page 62

3-SECOND BIOGRAPHY
JERZY NEYMAN
1894–1981
Polish mathematician and statistician who introduced the idea of confidence interval in 1937. His groundbreaking work in randomized experiments, sampling and hypothesis testing formed the basis for modern advanced techniques

30-SECOND TEXT
Joyce Kafui Klu

Retailers use confidence interval to help them make decisions about stock levels, such as how many items of different sizes to stock.

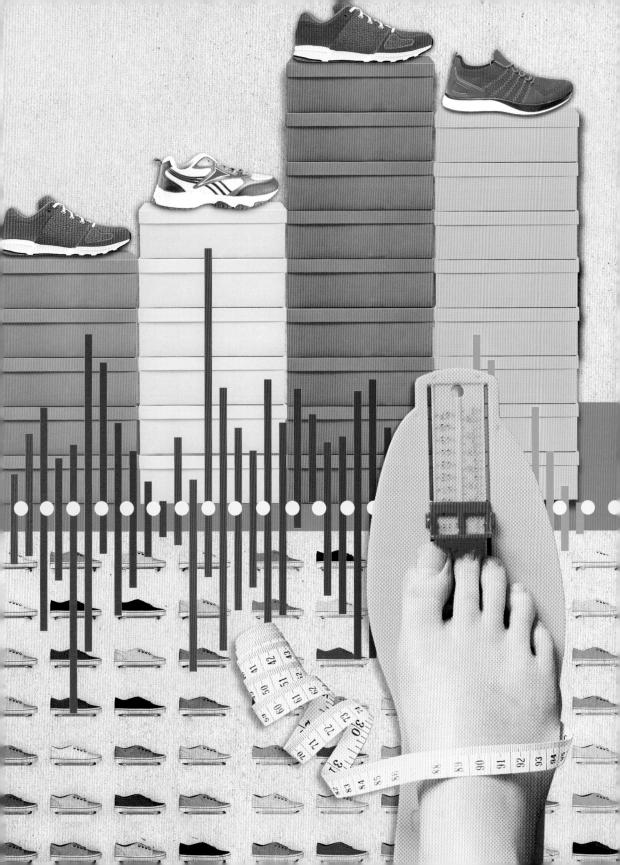

BOOTSTRAPPING

the 30-second calculation

Bootstrapping is a way of

drawing samples over and over again from the same dataset. Bootstrapping generates multiple versions of dataset from which values of computed parameters can be compared to understand the variability of estimated parameters. For example, to estimate the average age of smokers in a community, it may be practically impossible to interview every single individual (the population), so a random sample of individuals are interviewed instead. Now, how confident can one be that the estimated average using the sample is close to that of the population? As it's impractical to take samples again and again, bootstrapping provides a means of generating many different samples from the initially collected sample with replacement. Assuming the ages of five smokers are {18,21,25,28,31}, many (1000s of) bootstrap samples can be drawn from this data; {21,25,21,21,28}, {21,25,18,21,28}, {21,25,21,25,28}, {18,25,21,21,18}, {31,25,21,31,28}, and so on. The idea of bootstrapping is to generate many versions of a dataset to understand the stability of estimated results. Bootstrapping is particularly useful in situations where data is limited or difficult to acquire. The initial sample must be representative of the population so that the samples drawn are comparable to the population.

RELATED TOPICS
See also
POPULATION & SAMPLES
page 40

SAMPLING
page 42

CONFIDENCE INTERVAL
page 70

PERMUTATIONS &
COMBINATIONS
page 120

3-SECOND COUNT
Bootstrapping is a statistical technique of sampling from the same dataset multiple times to ascertain the variability (distribution) of an estimate.

3-MINUTE TOTAL
Due to the sensitive nature of most medical data, medical researchers rely on bootstrapping techniques. In most cases, the data obtained is too small for analysis and requires the use of bootstrap samples. The generated bootstrap samples are used to estimate standard deviations and confidence intervals, from which the distribution and variability associated with an unknown parameter of interest is analysed.

3-SECOND BIOGRAPHY
BRADLEY EFRON
1938–
American statistician who first proposed the technique of bootstrap resampling. His work has impacted the field of statistics as a whole and its areas of application

30-SECOND TEXT
Joyce Kafui Klu

Advanced computing technology has improved the time and resources needed to generate many bootstrap samples for analysis.

STANDARD ERROR

the 30-second calculation

The standard error is closely related to, but not to be confused with, the idea of a standard deviation. Often in statistics we take a sample (i.e. we select some members from a larger population) and calculate statistics of that sample to infer something about the population as a whole. For example, we can take the mean of our sample. However, if we were to take a different sample (selecting different members of the overall population), then we would obtain a different mean, and so on. Note that each sample also has its own standard deviation. But none of the obtained sample means is equal to the population mean, which is what we really want to know. However, intuitively, as the sample size gets bigger (with respect to the population size) we would expect the sample mean to become closer to the population mean (after all, once the sample size and population size are equal the two are one and the same). This idea is captured in the definition of the standard error of the mean (SEM). The SEM is calculated as $SEM = \sigma/\sqrt{n}$. Here n is the size of the sample and σ can be either the population standard deviation (giving the exact SEM) or the sample standard deviation (giving an approximation to the SEM).

3-SECOND COUNT
The standard error measures the degree of variability of a statistic. The statistic in question is often the mean, in which case we have the 'standard error of the mean'.

3-MINUTE TOTAL
The standard error of the mean is similar to – and often confused with – the standard deviation. The standard deviation describes the variability of a set of measurements. On the other hand, to describe the uncertainty associated with the estimate of the mean (of a population based on the mean of a sample), we use the standard error of the mean.

RELATED TOPICS
See also
POPULATION & SAMPLES
page 40

SAMPLING
page 42

MEAN
page 60

STANDARD DEVIATION
page 62

30-SECOND TEXT
David Pontin

Calculating a statistic for a sample rather than a whole population leads to the idea of standard error.

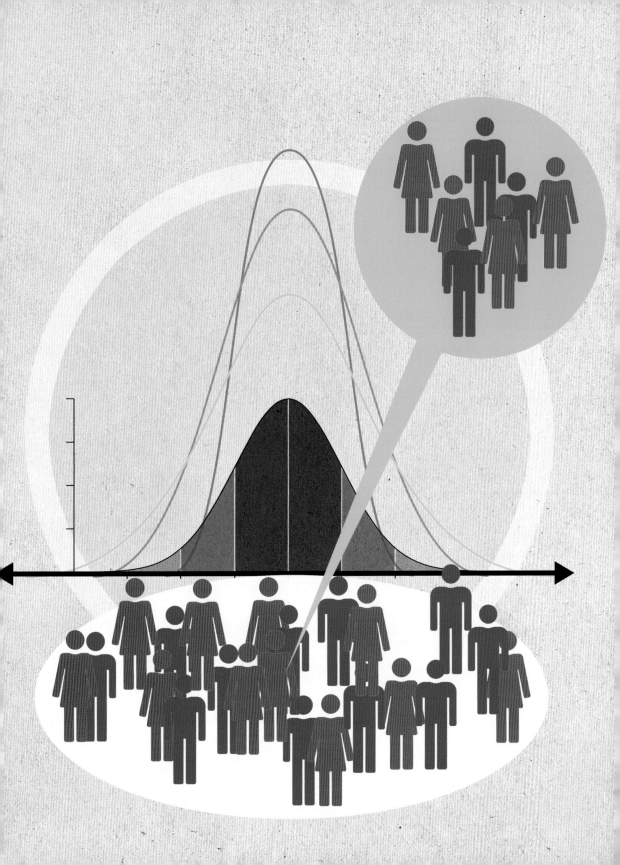

LINEAR REGRESSION & CORRELATION

the 30-second calculation

3-SECOND COUNT
Linear regression examines the dependence of the expected value of a variable on one or more other variables. Correlation measures the interdependence between variables.

3-MINUTE TOTAL
Linear regression is employed in financial settings to analyse commodity pricing; in economics to relate important indicators such as (un)employment, inflation and GDP; in medical statistics to influence health spending policy; in the military and in numerous other settings. Correlation is similarly used, but is open to abuse.

Linear regression and correlation are related statistical approaches to determining how variables depend on one another. Linear regression seeks to express the expected value of a dependent variable in terms of one or more known independent variables. Correlation describes a relationship between variables that is symmetrical, with none necessarily dependent or independent. Simple linear regression refers to the case of a single independent variable. With two variables, the data can be represented by a 2-D scatter graph. The approach is to describe the relationship by finding the straight line which best fits the data, by some measure. The most common measure is that of *ordinary least squares*, which seeks to minimize the sum of the squares of deviations of observed data points from the line; but other measures are also used. Correlation between two variables is the amount one changes, on average, when the other changes by a certain amount. Linear regression is typically used when the independent variable is manipulated by the experimenter; for example, time, concentration, etc. Correlation, on the other hand, is more often used when the experimenter measures both variables. Correlation is not causation: the sales of ice cream and sun cream may be correlated but one does not cause the other.

RELATED TOPICS
See also
STATISTICS
page 38

INDEPENDENT & DEPENDENT VARIABLES
page 44

MEAN
page 60

HYPOTHESIS TESTING
page 88

3-SECOND BIOGRAPHY
KARL PEARSON
1857–1936
English mathematician for whom the widely used correlation coefficient is named. He founded the world' first university statistics department at University College London

30-SECOND TEXT
John McDermott

There may be a near-straight line relationship between correlated variables.

PROBABILITY & RISK

algorithm A mathematical or computational method used to achieve a result.

critical value A value taken from a statistical distribution as a threshold for determining whether a test statistic is more extreme or not than expected.

false positive/negative A prediction given as true when it should be false or false when it should be true.

Fermat's Last Theorem Conjecture posed by French mathematician Pierre de Fermat in 1637, which states that no three positive integers a, b, and c satisfy the equation $a^n + b^n = c^n$ for any integer value of n greater than 2. No proof of the Theorem existed until 1994.

Fermat's Little Theorem Theorem that states that for a given prime number, p, and an integer, a, then $a^p - a$ is an integer multiple of p.

Fermat's Principle of Least Time Principle that states that light will always travel between two points using the path that takes least time.

Fermat's Two-square Theorem The set of Pythagorean primes where the prime number is the sum of two squares.

machine learning A statistical and computational algorithm that learns features from data through trial and error of known data.

null hypothesis The default assumption of an experiment that there is no relationship between the variables under observation.

objective probability The probability that something will occur based on factual or observed historical data.

petabyte A value of 2^{50} bytes, abbreviated as PB.

subjective probability The probability that something will occur based on experience or knowledge.

PROBABILITY

the 30-second calculation

Probability provides a

measurement of the chance or likelihood that a specific event will occur. The probability is calculated between 0 (no chance of occurrence) and 1 (it is certain that the event will occur). The higher the probability that the event occurs, the closer to 1 it becomes. For example, the probability of getting heads or tails on a fair coin (one which has heads and tails) is 0.5 or 50%. Probability can be viewed from largely two different perspectives. The first is objective or frequentist probability, where the probability of an event happening is described by the relative frequency of occurrence of the event in a scientifically repetitive set of experiments. This generates a number to objectively describe the probability. The second is subjective probability, the most popular of which is a Bayesian probability where expert knowledge as well as experimental data are used to determine the probability of an event occurring. Expert knowledge is determined by a prior probability which is subjective, experimental data is incorporated as a likelihood ratio and these are multiplied together to calculate odds of the event occurring. Bayesian probability is used in forensic science in the provision of expert evidence to the courts, as well as in many other applications where risk is being ascertained.

RELATED TOPICS
See also
STATISTICS
page 38

BAYESIAN PROBABILITY
page 90

3-SECOND BIOGRAPHY
GEROLAMO CARDANO
1501–76
Italian polymath who was interested in the natural sciences including physics, biology and chemistry as well as mathematics; credited with being one of the key founders of what we now understand as probability

30-SECOND TEXT
Niamh Nic Daéid

3-SECOND COUNT
Probability is a general term used to describe an area of mathematics that relates to calculating the likelihood or chance of something happening.

3-MINUTE TOTAL
The use of probabilistic analysis emerged around the mid-seventeenth century when a more precise and theoretical underpinning emerged to the concept of defining the chance of events occurring. The first textbook on probability theory was published in 1718 by Abraham de Moivre, a French mathematician.

Tossing a coin has a 50% probability of getting heads or tails as the outcome.

c. late 1607
Born in Beaumont-de-
Lomagne, France

1626
Graduates in civil law
from the University of
Orléans

1627
Works as a high court
attorney in Bordeaux

1629
Restores Apollonius's
plane loci (now known as
Apollonius' problem)

1631
Sworn into the office of
a councillor at the High
Court of Toulouse

1638
Appointed to a higher
chamber at the High
Court of Toulouse

1652
Promoted to the highest
level at the criminal court
of Toulouse

12 January 1665
Dies in Castres, France

PIERRE DE FERMAT

Pierre de Fermat was a French lawyer and mathematician in the early seventeenth century. He received his education in civil law and practised law at the High Court of Toulouse. After graduating at the age of 18, he moved to Bordeaux as a high court attorney. It was around this period that he began to do some high level mathematics. His interest in mathematics was more of a passionate hobby carried out during his spare time, and so most of his findings were not formally published. Most of his work came to light through his correspondence with other mathematicians and notes found after his death.

Fermat is known for being the first to discover the mathematical approach to finding the greatest and the smallest ordinates of curved lines, termed today as differential calculus. He is regarded as one of the founding fathers of probability theory, along with Blaise Pascal. Together, they laid the foundation for the modern theory of probability.

Fermat's interest in mathematics spanned the fields of number theory, analytic geometry, probability and optics. He made significant and novel contributions to all of these areas. He is famous for a number of novel theorems, including Fermat's last theorem, Fermat's principle or principle of least time, Fermat's two-square theorem and Fermat's little theorem.

His principle of least time, which can be used to describe the refraction of light rays, formed the basis on which the 'principle of least action', one of the most significant principles in modern physics, was formulated. Fermat is particularly remembered for 'Fermat's last theorem', which mathematicians struggled to prove for more than 300 years, until 1994 when Sir Andrew Wiles, a British mathematician, first published a complete proof of the theorem.

Fermat was minimally recognized as a mathematician during his lifetime due to his reluctance to publish, but his ideas, which he communicated through writing and shared with others, kept his work alive and continue to impact modern mathematics and physics. Isaac Newton acknowledged the impact of Fermat's work as the source of his early ideas about calculus, stating that it came directly from Fermat's way of drawing tangents.

Joyce Kafui Klu

PREDICTION

the 30-second calculation

Knowing what will happen in the future would allow us to make perfect decisions. This is impossible, of course, but just being able to estimate the probability of certain events can be greatly beneficial when planning for the future. Prediction in statistics revolves around finding dependencies between variables, so that if we gain information about them now then we have a better idea about how they will behave in the future. Ideally, we do this by identifying a *causal* relationship and monitoring the causal factor to predict the events that it will cause. However, in the real world, it is challenging to be able to prove causality because of the large number of other changing factors that may also affect what is being measured. Machine learning attempts to make predictions by discovering complex patterns in data that would be very hard for the human brain to recognize. Petabytes of data can be processed to create and update predictions of things such as stock prices and social media trends, which is invaluable information for hedge funds and marketing companies. Since automated predictions have such an influential role in modern society, it is important for algorithm design teams to also be ethically responsible. While machines are capable of data processing on levels that humans are not, it is difficult to program simple moral rules that we take for granted.

RELATED TOPICS

See also
LINEAR REGRESSION &
CORRELATION
page 76

MACHINE LEARNING
page 132

3-SECOND COUNT

Prediction aims to determine the occurrence of future events, often using our knowledge of the past and present. It is a key goal in statistical analysis.

3-MINUTE TOTAL

An example of unintended discrimination comes in using algorithms to predict crime hotspots and an individual's crime risk for more targeted policing. It is argued that the current use of such algorithms can encourage racial profiling without accountability and therefore must be used transparently.

3-SECOND BIOGRAPHY
JOHN GRAUNT
1620–74
English haberdasher who is credited with creating the first life table – a prediction of an individual's survival probability for the upcoming year based on their current age

30-SECOND TEXT
Harry Gray

Information is constantly churned into models that attempt to predict the future.

HYPOTHESIS TESTING

the 30-second calculation

3-SECOND COUNT
Hypothesis testing uses statistical procedures to determine whether a hypothesis is true, placing the burden of proof on the researcher making the claim.

3-MINUTE TOTAL
In a courtroom the presumption of innocence is the null hypothesis and its rejection is the alternative, of guilt. In this setting, type I errors are typically more strenuously avoided than type II: 'It is better that ten guilty persons escape than that one innocent suffer.' (Blackstone).

A statistical hypothesis is a

statement about a population which may or may not be true; hypothesis testing involves testing this statement. A claim that 'an immunization programme has reduced the measles infection rate in a community from 20%', is an example of such a hypothesis. The researcher forms the *null hypothesis* – for example, 'the infection rate remains at 20%' – often with the aim or hope of finding enough evidence to reject this in favour of the *alternative hypothesis* – 'the infection rate has decreased from 20%'. The test involves calculation of a *test statistic* based on sample data. This is compared to a *critical value* derived from a standard statistical distribution, together with a reliability requirement – the *confidence level* – set by the researcher. There is a trade-off between confidence in the result and its precision: absolute confidence that the infection rate lies between 0% and 100% is useless. The result of a hypothesis test may be wrong. A type I error is one in which the null hypothesis is wrongly rejected in favour of the claim in the alternative – the immunization programme is wrongly found to be effective when the infection rate is unchanged. A type II error is one in which the null hypothesis is wrongly accepted – the immunization programme has reduced the infection rate but the test concludes incorrectly that the programme does not work.

RELATED TOPICS
See also
STATISTICAL DISTRIBUTIONS
page 46

CONFIDENCE INTERVAL
page 70

FALSE POSITIVES & FALSE NEGATIVES
page 118

30-SECOND TEXT
John McDermott

A claim that a medicine is effective is a hypothesis that may be tested.

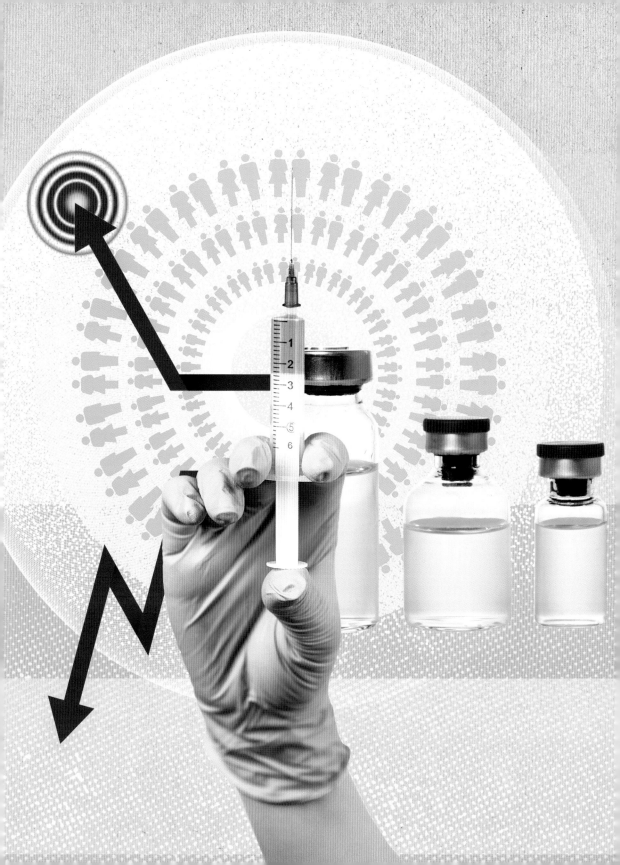

BAYESIAN PROBABILITY

the 30-second calculation

3-SECOND COUNT
Bayesian probability can be thought of as an individual's degree of belief in an event occurring.

3-MINUTE TOTAL
Through the Bayesian 'prior' degree of belief, subjective information about events can be included in statistical models to improve analysis. However, without due diligence, this subjectivity can incorporate unnecessary bias that instead leads to an inaccurate posterior belief.

Imagine asking a room of 1,000 people if they believe that a certain coin is fair (equal chance of heads or tails) before tossing it. Most people would say yes based on what they know about the majority of coins, despite knowing nothing about this particular coin. How many people would change their mind if the coin was tossed five times and they were all heads? Some people might but others might attribute it to luck. How about ten heads in a row? Those people who swapped before ten heads would now be confident in their belief that the coin is unfair, and sceptics might have changed but still be doubtful. All of these people have their own belief about the fairness of the coin. This idea is mathematically formalized in what is known as Bayes' theorem. Bayes' theorem relates the conditional probabilities of two events together. Conceptually, it can be described as obtaining a new (posterior) degree of belief in an event by combining your current (prior) degree of belief with an observation of another event (evidence) – some people believe that this is the natural way that humans think and learn. Philosophically, the Bayesian idea of probability is different from what we call frequentist probability. The Bayesian versus frequentist approach to probability is a long-standing debate among statisticians.

RELATED TOPICS
See also
STATISTICAL DISTRIBUTIONS
page 46

PROBABILITY
page 82

CONDITIONAL PROBABILITY
page 94

3-SECOND BIOGRAPHY
THOMAS BAYES
1702–61
English statistician whose notes on 'inverse' probability were published posthumously, later giving rise to what we call Bayes' theorem

30-SECOND TEXT
Harry Gray

Our posterior belief is obtained based on the strength of prior knowledge and the observed evidence.

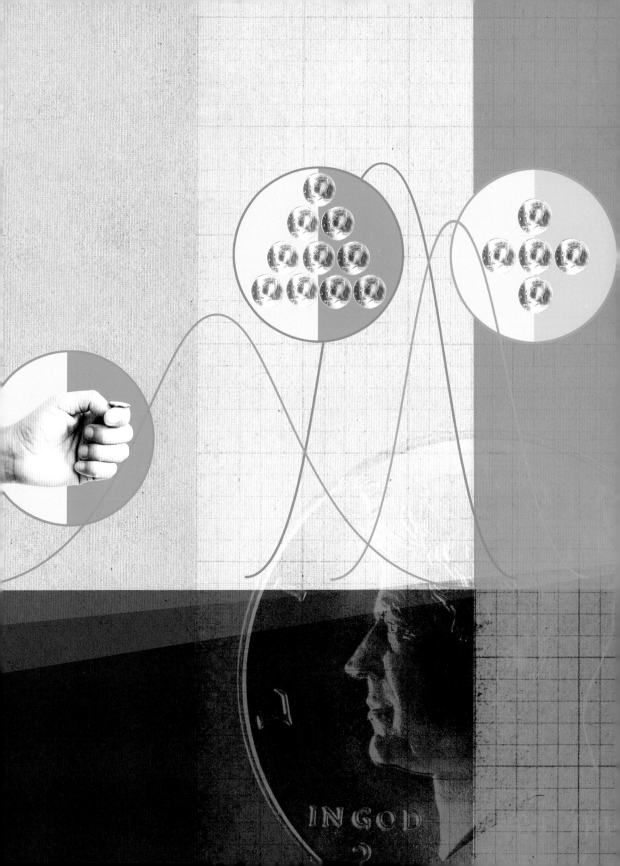

c. 1702
Born in London

1719
Studies logic and
theology at the
University of Edinburgh

1722
Assists his Presbyterian
minister father at a
chapel in London

1731
Publishes the *Divine
Benevolence; or, an
Attempt to Prove That
the Principal End of the
Divine Providence and
Government is the
Happiness of His
Creatures*

1734
Becomes minister of the
Mount Sion chapel in
Tunbridge Wells, Kent

1736
Anonymously publishes
*An Introduction to the
Doctrine of Fluxions, and
a Defence of the
Mathematicians Against
the Objections of the
Author of The Analyst*
– a defence of the logical
foundations of calculus

1742
Elected as a fellow of
the Royal Society

1761
Dies in Tunbridge Wells,
Kent

1763
Posthumous publication
of the essay 'Towards
Solving a Problem in the
Doctrine of Chances'
in the *Philosophical
Transactions of the
Royal Society*

THOMAS BAYES

Thomas Bayes was the son of a Presbyterian minister and later became a nonconformist who followed the protestant religious beliefs but refused to conform to the rites and ceremonies as laid down in the Book of Common Prayer.

He studied theology and logic at the University of Edinburgh in 1719, where it is thought he was influenced in this thinking by reading the work of Abraham de Moivre and David Hume. He later followed a theological pathway, becoming the Reverend at Mount Sion chapel in Tunbridge Wells, Kent.

Bayes is best known for establishing a mathematical basis for inference, which incorporated the frequency of prior events into the calculation that the event will occur in the future. His essay describing this argument – 'Towards Solving a Problem in the Doctrine of Chances' – was published in the Philosophical Transactions of the Royal Society after his death and gave rise to a theorem that carried his name. Little more detail is known about Bayes' life, but his ideas have had a major influence on subsequent developments in statistics and probability. The Bayes' theorem and Bayesian statistics can be used in many applications, from medical testing to financial risk assessment. The Bayesian approach is also applied in the world of forensic science, most notably in the interpretation of DNA evidence.

Bayes is buried in Bunhill Fields burial ground in London, which is fittingly close to the premises of the Royal Statistical Society.

Niamh Nic Daéid

CONDITIONAL PROBABILITY

the 30-second calculation

It is an intuitive idea that certain events occurring can affect the chance of others occurring. Conditional probability is the formal mathematical construction to describe this intuitive idea. Situations that involve conditional probability appear frequently when playing games. Imagine a two-player dice game in which player two rolls a dice first, followed by player one doing the same. The rule is that if player two gets a higher number on their roll then they win, otherwise player one wins. Before player two rolls, their probability of winning is 5/12 (roughly 42%). Suppose player two then rolls the dice and gets a five. The probability that they will win changes to 2/3 (66%), since player one can only roll either a 5 or 6 to win. Here we have conditioned on the event that player two rolls a 5 and, in that situation, the probability of player two now winning the game increases. However, if the event that we are conditioning on is independent of the event whose probability we wish to calculate, then the conditional probability remains the same as if we hadn't seen the other event. An example of that in the same game is if we condition on which day of the week it is. Clearly the day of the week does not affect which numbers will appear on either dice and therefore does not affect the game in any way, so the probabilities remain unchanged.

3-SECOND COUNT
Conditional probability is the probability of an event occurring while assuming that other different events have already occurred.

3-MINUTE TOTAL
The Monty Hall problem is a famous example of conditional probability. With a prize behind one of three doors, players can select one door. An empty door is opened, and the player is given the choice to switch to the other unopened door. Switching increases the player's chance of winning.

RELATED TOPICS
See also
INDEPENDENT & DEPENDENT VARIABLES
page 44

PROBABILITY
page 82

BAYESIAN PROBABILITY
page 90

3-SECOND BIOGRAPHY
PIERRE DE FERMAT
1607–65
French lawyer and mathematician famous for posing Fermat's Last Theorem, a mathematical conjecture that went unsolved until 1994, when it was proven by English mathematician Andrew Wiles

30-SECOND TEXT
Harry Gray

The probability of events may change based on what we have already seen.

LIKELIHOOD RATIO

the 30-second calculation

30-SECOND TEXT
Harry Gray

3-SECOND COUNT
The likelihood ratio is a statistic that is used to compare the probability of an event occurring under two different circumstances.

3-MINUTE TOTAL
In 2010, the widely used method of mammography screening for breast cancer detection was estimated to have a positive likelihood ratio of 5.9 and negative likelihood ratio of 0.3 for women under 40 years old.

The likelihood ratio is computed

by taking the ratio of the likelihood of an event conditional on two different circumstances. If it is large, then the likelihood of the event under the first circumstance is far greater than the likelihood of the event under the second circumstance, and vice versa. It is popular in diagnostic testing where it is used to assess the utility of performing a test, since test results are almost never 100% certain. For example, suppose a test is 99% accurate at giving a correctly positive result when someone has a disease. It is also 90% accurate at giving a correctly negative result when someone does not have the disease, meaning that it will incorrectly give a positive result when someone does not have the disease 10% of the time. The positive likelihood ratio is then the ratio of the probability that the test is positive given that they do have the disease compared with the probability that the test is positive given that they don't have the disease, which is $0.99/0.1 = 9.9$. This means that if someone has the disease, then the test is 9.9 times more likely to give a positive result than if the person did not have the disease, which is reassuring for our confidence in the test. Note that the likelihood ratio has not told us the probability that the person does actually have the disease when we receive the test result.

The size of the likelihood ratio updates the post-test probability of disease.

ABSOLUTE RISK

the 30-second calculation

3-SECOND COUNT
An absolute risk is an estimate of the odds of an event occurring over a specified timeframe.

3-MINUTE TOTAL
A 2018 *Lancet* study showed that 15–95-year olds who drink one daily alcoholic drink increased their one-year risk of an alcohol-related health problem by 0.5%. Since 914 of 100,000 people experience an alcohol-related health problem anyway (e.g. diabetes), this increase for moderate drinkers equates to four extra people per 100,000.

Absolute risk is calculated using the number of times an event occurred in a group of interest divided by the total population of that group. Even though this seems fairly simple, in reality getting a good estimate for the absolute risk of a disease, for example, involves combining multiple large medical studies that were conducted on thousands of people across multiple years. Absolute risk is an effective way of describing risks because it puts the frequency of an event in the context of the overall population in which it was observed, which is usually easier to understand. This ease of understanding can increase patient agency in medical decision-making. Suppose there is a medical treatment that leads to a full recovery from a disease for five people in every 100, compared with the previous treatment, which cured one out of every 100 people. The side-effects of the new treatment can now be weighed by the knowledge that it saves an extra four in 100 people. The *relative risk* framing of the same statistic reports a five-times increase in efficacy for the new treatment, which might be seen as overstating its benefits when the absolute risk measure is known. Absolute risk is sometimes incorrectly presented without reference to the underlying population, which can make the corresponding risk seem misleadingly small or large.

RELATED TOPICS
See also
RELATIVE RISK
page 100

COMPARING NUMBERS
page 138

3-SECOND BIOGRAPHY
DAVID SPIEGELHALTER
1953–
British statistician and Winton Professor of the Public Understanding of Risk at the University of Cambridge, widely known for helping to shape media reporting of statistics and risk information

30-SECOND TEXT
Harry Gray

Absolute risk presents the risk of an event in the context of the population observed.

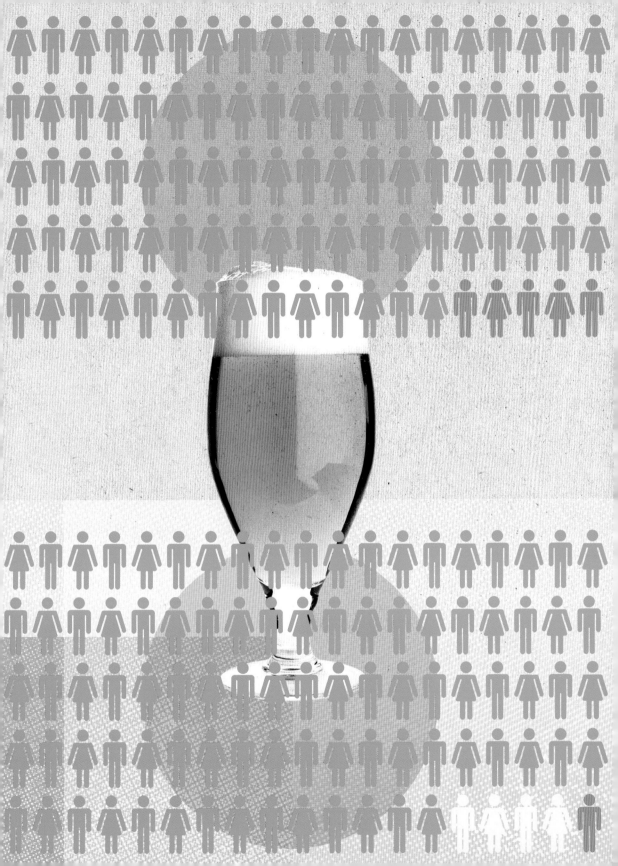

RELATIVE RISK

the 30-second calculation

Relative risk, also known as the risk ratio, is calculated using the ratio of absolute risks between two groups for an event. It is useful because it gives an idea of how much more or less likely one group is than the other to experience an event of interest. In medical statistics, it is used to show how much more likely an experiment group, such as people who smoke, is to experience a health-related condition compared with a control group who do not. A heavy criticism of the relative risk in reporting experimental outcomes is that it does not provide a baseline of the event's overall prevalence in the control group. For example, a relative risk of 100, which means that the risk of the experiment group is 100 times higher than the other, seems highly meaningful. However, if the absolute risk of the control group is that the event only affects one in 1 billion people, then the absolute risk for the experiment group (even though it is 100 times higher) is still very low and could be considered negligible. Much like the misuse of absolute risks, high relative risks presented in isolation can suggest the risk is much higher than it actually is. This is particularly important to avoid in medicine because it can impact the health-related decisions that people make. Good practice in reporting is to present the relative risk next to its underlying absolute risk to give the full picture.

RELATED TOPICS
See also
ABSOLUTE RISK
page 98

COMPARING NUMBERS
page 138

30-SECOND TEXT
Harry Gray

3-SECOND COUNT
A relative risk is an estimate of the change in risk for a certain event between two groups.

3-MINUTE TOTAL
In 2011, bacon sandwiches made headlines in the UK for allegedly increasing the risk of bowel cancer by 20% (if consumed daily). This scary statistic was widely scrutinized by risk communicators, since its overall absolute risk was an increase of just 1 (from 5 to 6) in 100 people.

Relative risks can be put into perspective using data from two absolute risks.

NUMERICAL BIAS

the 30-second calculation

Numerical bias is an established concept in statistical estimation. It can have a range of different causes, such as non-random sampling or using models that are too simple, each of which can have different effects. Scientific experiments and statistical models are generally designed to minimize numerical bias, but it can easily go unnoticed. An example of numerical bias in everyday life arises in electronic timetables at bus stops. When there is no traffic, the timetable seems to do very well at estimating the arrival time of the next bus. However, when there is heavy traffic the story is different. This is because the speed of the traffic is not accounted for by the tracking system on the bus, only its current location. The arrival estimate is only accurate when there is no traffic, leading to the frustrating situation of '5 mins' being shown on the timetable for much longer than a single minute. This estimate is numerically biased because it is systematically underestimating the actual time till the bus arrives during traffic. Numerical bias is not always a bad thing, though. If the bus is always 10 minutes late, then we can adjust for this by getting to the stop 9 minutes later than usual and only wait for 1 minute. However, if the bus always arrives randomly up to 10 minutes late, then we should decide to arrive on time, but could be waiting for up to 10 minutes.

RELATED TOPICS
See also
POPULATION & SAMPLES
page 40

SAMPLING
page 42

MEASUREMENT ERROR
page 64

3-SECOND COUNT
Numerical bias is a statistical term for when a mathematical quantity systematically differs from the actual quantity that it is intended to represent.

3-MINUTE TOTAL
Numerical bias is an important thing to be aware of when computing statistics as it leads to inaccuracies. These inaccuracies can have dramatic consequences when estimating the effectiveness of a new drug or trying to predict a political election result.

3-SECOND BIOGRAPHY
CHARLES STEIN
1920–2016
American statistician whose work on biased estimation challenged the traditional statistical thinking that bias was always bad

30-SECOND TEXT
Harry Gray

Bus arrival times that are estimated without allowing for traffic are likely to be biased.

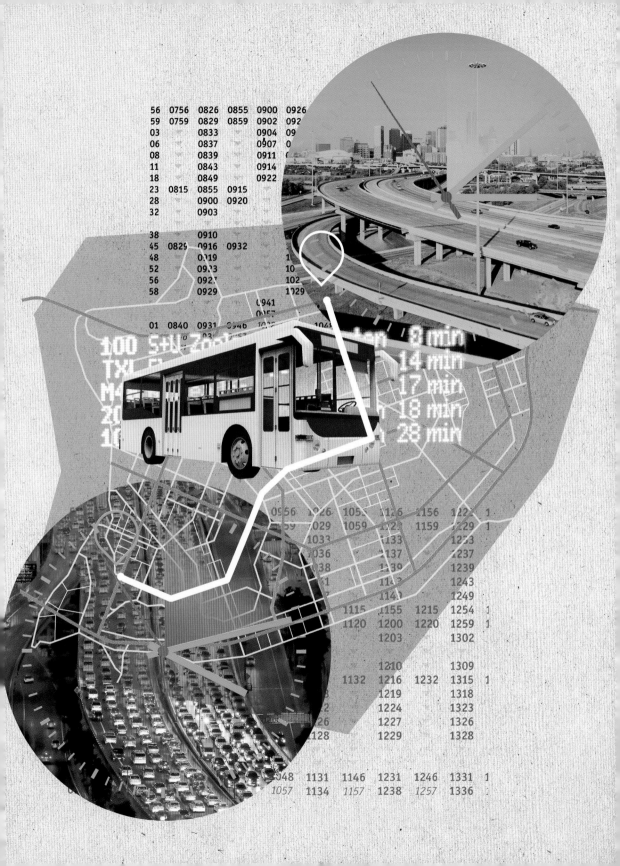

USING NUMBERS

base The number used for counting in a particular system, for example the decimal system has base 10.

binary A numerical system based on two digits: 1 and 0.

denominator In a simple fraction (one number over another) the denominator is the bottom number and cannot be zero.

e A mathematical constant, also called Euler's number, which is approximately equal to 2.71828. It is the number whose natural logarithm is 1.

greatest common divisor (GCD) The largest positive integer that divides into two other integers.

irrational number A number that cannot be represented as a simple fraction.

machine learning A statistical and computational algorithm that learns features from data through trial and error of known data.

n! A factorial of *n*. Where all positive whole numbers up to *n* are multiplied together.

natural logarithm A logarithm to base e.

numerator In a simple fraction, the numerator is the top number.

place-value A system of writing and giving value to numbers based on the relative position of their digits.

whole number A number with no decimal point or fraction, also called an integer.

NUMERICAL BASES

the 30-second calculation

A numerical base corresponds to
the number of different digits, including 0, in a
positional number system. Our usual base ten
system runs from 0 to 9 and then repeats,
without confusion, by shifting a digit into a new
position. After counting ten of something, we
can count up to ten lots of ten, and then move
to ten lots of those, and so on. We owe this
system to having ten fingers. The number 123
usually means 1 hundred plus 2 tens plus 3 –
this is implied by the positions of the digits.
Writing numbers in this way – called 'place-
value' – is efficient, since it avoids requiring
new symbols for each number; each position
represents a power of ten. Other bases work in
the same way, by representing numbers in units
and then increasing powers of the base, as they
shift to the right. Had we evolved with eight
fingers we might count in base eight, and write
the number 123 to represent 1 sixty-four
(sixty-four is eight eights) plus 2 eights plus 3.
To write a number unambiguously in a base other
than the usual ten the base may be used as a
subscript, for example 123_8. Any whole number
greater than one can be the base for a positional
number system. The ancient Babylonians used
base 60, which has echoes in our counting of
seconds and minutes. Computers represent
numbers internally using base two, known as
binary. The digits in binary are just 0 and 1.

3-SECOND COUNT
A numerical base is the
number used for counting
in a particular system. We
usually count in tens (base
ten), but base two (in
computing) and others
are used.

3-MINUTE TOTAL
At the most fundamental
level, computers use binary
– base two. Base 16, using
digits 0–9 along with A–F,
is used in numerical
internet identifiers. Other
bases such as 12 (inches
and hours) and 60 (seconds
and minutes) persist in
our culture and language.

RELATED TOPICS
See also
POWERS & ROOTS
page 30

LOGARITHMS
page 110

3-SECOND BIOGRAPHY
GOTTFRIED WILHELM LEIBNIZ
1646–1716
German polymath who
invented the binary number
system now used in computing

30-SECOND TEXT
John McDermott

*We count using base
ten but computers
count in base two.*

LOGARITHMS

the 30-second calculation

A logarithm is a quantity

representing the power to which a fixed positive number, the base, must be raised to produce a given target number. That is, it tells us how many of the base we must multiply together to produce the target. For example, the logarithm in base 2 of 8 is 3, since $2 \times 2 \times 2 = 2^3 = 8$. Logarithms are written using the abbreviation 'log' and the base as a subscript, so that 'the logarithm in base 2 of 8 is 3' is shortened to '$\log_2 (8) = 3$'. The value of a logarithm need not always be a whole number; for example, $\log_2 (10)$ is approximately 3.313. Logarithms in base 10 are widely used to reduce the size of numbers involved in calculations with and display of data, since $\log_{10} (100) = 2$, $\log_{10} (1000) = 3$, and so on. Tables of logarithms facilitated complex calculations in the days before the widespread availability of calculators and computers. Such calculations were vital in navigation, engineering, medicine, science and technology. The (so-called) irrational number e, which is approximately 2.718, is known as the base of the *natural logarithm*. The natural logarithm has its own notation so that, for example, $\log_e (8)$ and $\log_e (10)$ are usually written ln (8) and ln (10). This special treatment is earned by the vital role e plays in calculus, probability and numerous other branches of mathematics.

RELATED TOPICS
See also
IRRATIONAL NUMBERS
page 18

POWERS & ROOTS
page 30

NUMERICAL BASES
page 108

3-SECOND BIOGRAPHY
JOHN NAPIER
1550–1617
Scottish mathematician who invented logarithms. He also popularized the use of the decimal point in representing numbers

30-SECOND TEXT
John McDermott

3-SECOND COUNT
The logarithm of a positive number relative to another number, the base, is the power to which the base must be raised to give that positive number.

3-MINUTE TOTAL
Logarithms are used to describe values that grow or shrink too fast to be easily compared or displayed otherwise. The Richter scale for measuring the strength of earthquakes is logarithmic: an earthquake scoring a 6 on this scale is approximately ten times as strong as one scoring a 5.

Logarithms aided calculations before computers but are still useful in understanding computing and big data

PERCENTAGES

the 30-second calculation

3-SECOND COUNT
A percentage describes a proportion, in parts per hundred, of a whole.

3-MINUTE TOTAL
To calculate percentages without a calculator, a useful trick is to first find 10% (divide by 10), and then smaller amounts such as 5% (divide in half again) and 1% (divide the 10% figure by 10 again). Then 17% = 10% + 5% + 1% + 1%, so 17% of 60 is 6 + 3 + 0.6 + 0.6 = 10.2.

Percentages represent parts of a whole, expressed in hundredths, and provide an alternative to the use of decimals or fractions. Twenty-five per cent (25%) is the same as 0.25 or 25/100, which is the same as a quarter, as there are four 25s in 100. To find 25% of another number, multiply by 0.25, or divide by four: 25% of 60 is one quarter of 60, i.e. 15. To find a more awkward percentage, convert to an equivalent decimal and multiply: 17% of 60 is $0.17 \times 60 = 10.2$. Underlying these basic calculations is a fact that sometimes causes confusion: percentages are relative. If a shop raises its prices by 10%, then an item previously costing £100 will now cost £110 (£100 plus 10% of £100). If the shop later sells the item at '10% off', the price will be £99 (£110 reduced by 10% of £110, i.e. by £11). The increase and reduction do not cancel exactly. Savings and borrowings are commonly subject to interest payments, measured in percentage rates. Interest may be applied simply, so that a rate of 5% per year on a loan of £100 for two years would see the borrower repay £100 + £10 (£5 for each year) at the end. However, interest is usually compounded, meaning that in the second year, the interest to be paid will be calculated on the total amount owed so far, i.e. it will not be £5 but 5% of (£100 + £5) = £5.25.

RELATED TOPICS
See also
RATIONAL NUMBERS
page 16

PROBABILITY
page 82

FRACTIONS
page 114

3-SECOND BIOGRAPHY
JACOB BERNOULLI
1655–1705
A member of a famous Swiss mathematical family, he discovered the hugely important constant, e – the base of the natural logarithm – while investigating the subject of compound interest

30-SECOND TEXT
John McDermott

Percentages are widely used to describe price changes, especially to trumpet retail discounts

FRACTIONS

the 30-second calculation

3-SECOND COUNT
A fraction is a number formed from one whole number divided by another, written with the first above the second and a bar between; for example, ¾ .

3-MINUTE TOTAL
Fractions are in everyday use in great variety – describing quantities of food in recipes or for sale, as well as price discounts and special offers. Fractions are depicted on fuel gauges and describe positions on sports fields, and of course we use them to tell the time.

Dividing one whole number by another gives a fraction. The first (top) number is called the *numerator* while the second (bottom) is the *denominator*. A fraction may represent a proportion, some parts of a whole, so ¾ represents three out of four equal parts. Three slices of a cake divided into four pieces is exactly as good as six slices of the same cake divided into eight; so ¾ = ⁶⁄₈. This works in general: multiplying or dividing top and bottom by the same number gives an equal fraction. A fraction in which the numerator is the larger number represents some whole unit(s) plus some fractional part. So ⁴⁄₃ may represent one whole cake and one third of another and may be written as 1⅓. Fractions can be added, subtracted, multiplied and divided. To add two fractions, first write them with a *common denominator*, then add the numerators. For example, to add ¾ and ⅝, first re-write ¾ as ⁶⁄₈, so the sum becomes ⁶⁄₈ + ⅝ = ¹¹⁄₈, or 1⅜. To multiply fractions, multiply the two numerators together and the two denominators together. So, ¾ × ⅝ = ³×⁵⁄₄×₈ = ¹⁵⁄₃₂. To divide one fraction by another, invert the second (switch its numerator and denominator) and then multiply this by the first. For example, ¾ ÷ ⅝ = ¾ × ⁸⁄₅ = ²⁴⁄₂₀, which can be simplified to ⁶⁄₅ = 1⅕.

RELATED TOPICS
See also
RATIONAL NUMBERS
page 16

PERCENTAGES
page 112

3-SECOND BIOGRAPHY
FIBONACCI
c. 1170–c. 1250
The way in which we write fractions – the 'bar' notation with one digit above the othe – was popularized by the Itali mathematician Fibonacci (rea name Leonardo of Pisa)

30-SECOND TEXT
John McDermott

Fractions are parts of a whole.

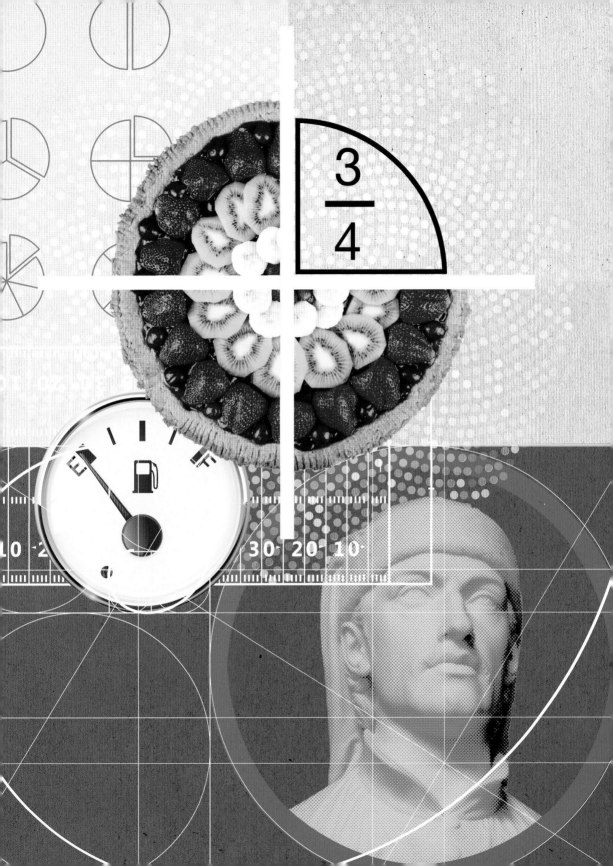

ALGORITHMS

the 30-second calculation

Algorithms specify how to solve classes of problems in mathematics and computer science. Examples include the Euclidean algorithm for finding the greatest common divisor (GCD) of two numbers, a whole class of algorithms for sorting data, and the process by which the shortest route from A to B is found by a satnav system. An algorithm is a procedure with precise step-by-step instructions to be followed in order. This procedure may have one or more inputs, such as the start and finish points of a journey, and it will produce the solution, such as the shortest route, as an output. Due to this precise and mechanical nature, algorithms are suited to automation by computer in the form of programs. They underpin the functionality of most modern technology, so that each time we use a touchscreen, make a call, start an application or press a button in a car, we rely on an algorithm to work. Two algorithms devised for the same class of problems may have different qualities, in terms of efficiency or the nature of the solutions produced. Deciding, in an automatic way, which to select to tackle a problem is a task for artificial intelligence. This in turn includes the area of machine learning, which uses algorithms to look for patterns in data and then adapts the behaviour in its programs accordingly.

RELATED TOPICS

See also
BIG DATA
page 128

ARTIFICIAL INTELLIGENCE
page 130

MACHINE LEARNING
page 132

3-SECOND BIOGRAPHY
MUHAMMAD IBN MUSA
AL-KHWARIZMI
c. 780–c. 850
Persian mathematician, astronomer and geographer, from whose name the word 'algorithm' derives

30-SECOND TEXT
John McDermott

3-SECOND COUNT
An algorithm is a procedure for solving a mathematical or computational problem in a finite number of steps.

3-MINUTE TOTAL
Algorithms are used in weather forecasting, to handle share transactions and to provide suggestions based on user likes for Amazon, Netflix, Spotify and others. Google's PageRank Algorithm determines the order in which search results are returned to the user and has been called the '50 trillion dollar algorithm'.

An algorithm is the recipe for a task suited to the working of a computer.

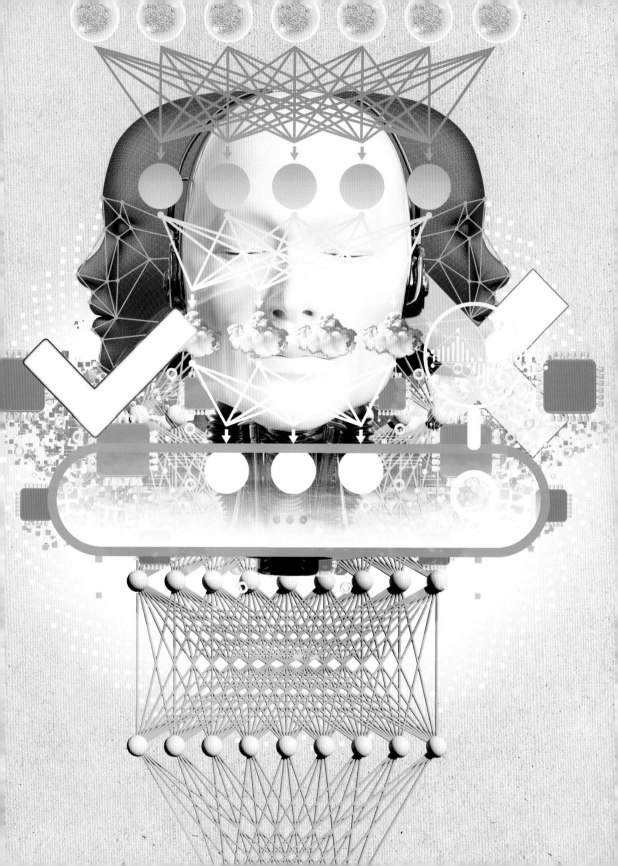

FALSE POSITIVES & FALSE NEGATIVES

the 30-second calculation

3-SECOND COUNT
A false positive occurs when a test wrongly indicates the presence of a condition. A false negative occurs when lack of the condition is wrongly indicated.

3-MINUTE TOTAL
False positives and negatives arise in settings including medicine, business and computing, but also in the legal arena. The counterintuitive dependence of rates of these errors on incidence of a condition in the population (the base rate), may lead to poor decision-making or judgements.

In a test with two possible

outcomes, such as a blood test for the presence of a disease, there are two types of error that can occur: a false positive, or *type I error*, which incorrectly indicates the presence of the disease, or a false negative, or *type II error*, which fails to detect that the disease is present. The relative importance of the types of error is highly dependent on context. Failure to detect a disease – a false negative – can be fatal; the cost of a false positive in an email spam filter – loss of a genuine email – probably won't be. Test reliability depends, in a non-intuitive way, on actual incidence of the condition. Suppose that a test is always correct for infected people, but only 99% of the time for people who are not infected. This test seems good, having a 0% false negative rate and 1% false positive rate. In a population of 1,000, if 20% are infected there will be 200 people with the disease, all correctly diagnosed – and 800 people without the disease, eight of whom will be incorrectly diagnosed as infected. The likelihood that a person diagnosed as having the disease actually has it is 200 in 208, or about 96%. Here the test works well. If the infection rate is a much lower 0.1%, then just one person in 1,000 has the disease. Of the 999 uninfected, approximately ten will be wrongly diagnosed. In this setting only 1 in 11, or 9%, of positive diagnoses is right.

RELATED TOPICS
See also
PROBABILITY
page 82

HYPOTHESIS TESTING
page 88

BAYESIAN PROBABILITY
page 90

CONDITIONAL PROBABILITY
page 94

3-SECOND BIOGRAPHY
DANIEL KAHNEMAN
1934–
Nobel prize-winning psychologist who helped to develop the cognitive psychology of human error due to bias

30-SECOND TEXT
John McDermott

The consequences of a false positive or negative may be alarming, or even deadly.

PERMUTATIONS & COMBINATIONS

the 30-second calculation

A permutation of a set is an arrangement of some or all members of the set. Counting the number of ways in which this can be done for a given set and selection size is fundamental to understanding statistics and probability. Given four tasks to be completed, in how many ways can the order be chosen? Any one of the four tasks could be chosen to be first, leaving any one of the remaining three to be chosen second. Then two tasks remain to be chosen as third and, finally, there is just one option – the remaining unchosen task – to be completed last. So the number of ways of ordering the tasks is $24 = 4 \times 3 \times 2 \times 1$. The product $4 \times 3 \times 2 \times 1$ has its own mathematical shorthand: 4! (pronounced 'four factorial'). To arrange three blue balls, one green ball and one red ball, two choices which differ only by a rearrangement of the blues (which can be done in 3! ways) are indistinguishable, so the number of different arrangements is $5!/3! = 20$. A combination of items is chosen from a set without regard to order. There are $8!/(3! \times (8 - 3)!) = 8!/(3! \times 5!)$ ways to choose three items from eight, since the number of rearrangements of the three chosen, or the remaining five not chosen, should be discounted. The general formula for choosing a combination of r items from n objects is $n!/(r! \times (n - r)!)$.

RELATED TOPICS
See also
POWERS & ROOTS
page 30

STATISTICS
page 38

PROBABILITY
page 82

3-SECOND BIOGRAPHY
ÉVARISTE GALOIS
1811–32
French mathematician who studied the permutations of roots of polynomials and founded the theory named for him, which underpins the branch of algebra known as group theory

30-SECOND TEXT
John McDermott

3-SECOND COUNT
A permutation is a selection of members from a set in a specific order. A combination is a selection from a set where the order does not matter.

3-MINUTE TOTAL
Permutations and combinations arise in biology, computing, optimization and probability, on which lotteries are based. Take a lottery draw that selects six numbers, disregarding order, from a set of 59. There are $59!/(6! \times 53!)$ ways of choosing these, giving 1 chance in more than 45 million of choosing the matching set.

Counting permutations or combinations allows us to understand probabilities.

c. 1170
Born Leonardo Pisano in Pisa, son to Guglielmo of the Bonacci family

1200
Finishes his travels around the Mediterranean and returns to Pisa

1202
Produces his famous work *Liber Abaci*

1220
Publishes *Practica Geometriae*

c. 1224
Presented to Frederick II, the Holy Roman Emperor and King of both Germany and Italy

1225
Produces *Flos* and *Liber quadratum*

1240
Awarded a salary by decree of the Republic of Pisa

c. 1250
Dies in Pisa

FIBONACCI

Fibonacci has been described as the greatest genius of number theory between the times of Diophantus of Alexandria (fourth century) and Pierre de Fermat (seventeenth century), both giants in the field.

Born to the Bonacci family in Pisa as Leonardo, Fibonacci acquired the name by which he is now known from a shortening of 'son of Bonacci'. During his early life, Fibonacci travelled around the Mediterranean with his father, a Pisan merchant. These travels earned him the name Leonardo Bigollo, meaning 'traveller' or 'wanderer'. His exposure to Arabic learning and specifically Hindu-Arabic mathematics in this time inspired a great part of his legacy.

On his return to Pisa, Fibonacci produced his most famous work, the *Liber Abaci* (Book of Calculation), which introduced to a wider European audience the 'nine Indian figures' (the digits 1–9) together with 0, and the place-value system we use today based on these digits. This system was superior to Roman numerals, being much more efficient for calculation.

The *Liber Abaci* addressed a broad range of mathematical problems, including Fibonacci's approach to a puzzle related to the growth of a rabbit population. His solution, which was surely known to Hindu scholars before him, was the sequence which now bears his name: 1, 1, 2, 3, 5, 8 . . . , and so on, in which each term is the sum of the previous two.

Every student of mathematics learns of the Fibonacci sequence. It has found application not only in mathematics but also across the sciences. It arises in nature, for example, in the arrangement of leaves on the stems of classes of plants, while the limit of ratios of its terms is the golden ratio, beloved of classical artists and architects. It has also entered popular culture – the book *The Da Vinci Code* relies on the sequence as a plot device.

During the 1220s, at the height of his fame and prowess, Fibonacci published several more works: *Practica Geometriae, Flos* and *Liber quadratum*, as well as others now lost. Fibonacci engaged in correspondence with the Holy Roman Emperor Frederick II and exchanged problems with Frederick's scholars.

Little is known of Fibonacci's later life. In 1240 the city of Pisa made 'Leonardo Bigollo' the award of a salary in recognition of his mathematical services. It is believed that he died in Pisa around 1250. A statue of him was erected in the city in the nineteenth century.

John McDermott

VISUALIZING NUMBERS

σ The Greek letter sigma, which in statistics often represents the standard deviation of a population.

algorithmic bias An implicit or explicit bias in software resulting in inconsistent or incorrect outputs.

artificial neural networks A statistical machine-learning method that mimics biological neurons in order to learn patterns in data.

Bayesian networks A graph of nodes and edges built with statistical priors which weight the importance of each piece of information in order to calculate the statistical likelihood of an outcome from a set of plausible inputs.

data-ink ratio A data visualization concept designed to maximize information while minimizing unnecessary content that may distract from the message.

decision tree A tree-like chart that splits complex classification problems into a series of decisions and their possible outcomes. Multiple decision trees are used in machine learning.

deep learning An extension of machine learning where the algorithm determines which features are important to learn without the need for human intervention, but with deeper and more complex networks.

dimensionality reduction A method of abstracting complex data into a simpler view for easier human interpretation.

genetic algorithms Machine-learning method that uses the biological concept of 'fitness' to determine winning solutions to a problem.

Gestalt laws Principles of human visual perception that aid the understanding of how to present informative data visualizations.

Internet of Things The addition of 'smart' features to primarily mundane domestic or industrial equipment such as fridges or kettles so that they can communicate with a server or with each other.

learning algorithms A computational method that is able to improve its performance of an objective function through trial and error.

scatter plot A plot of two continuous variables on x and y axes.

support vector machines A machine-learning method of mapping data patterns into high-order dimensions to maximize the classification of data into two groups.

BIG DATA

the 30-second calculation

3-SECOND COUNT
Big data describes sets of
data which are so large that
they cannot be analysed
by traditional data
processing means.

3-MINUTE TOTAL
Big data can be used to
model behaviour, trends
and interactions. The types
of datasets available are
being used to determine
the travel pathways
through our cities, trends
in health and well-being,
and what we watch, wear
and consume.

Big data is a generic term that
was first used in the 1990s to describe large
and complicated datasets. These sets of data
can also contain images and sounds as well as
numbers. The datasets are so large that they
need to be analysed often by using multiple
computers all working together at the same
time. Increasing world-wide access to the
internet, the development of the Internet
of Things (the online connection of devices
to each other) and the increasing use of digital
technologies in our homes and vehicles means
that the amount of data being generated
around the world on an hourly basis is simply
staggering. In 2017 there were an estimated
3.4 billion internet users; it's estimated that
by 2025 more than 70 billion devices will be
connected to the Internet of Things. Because of
the size of the datasets there are challenges in
how to capture, store, transfer, analyse, visualize
and manage the information. The data is often
described in terms of the quantity (or volume),
the types of data (or variety), the speed at
which the data is being generated (or velocity)
and the quality of the data (or veracity). Big data
presents big challenges and many organizations
are investing heavily in working out how to
manage these challenges into the future.

RELATED TOPIC
See also
TRENDS
page 140

3-SECOND BIOGRAPHY
KEVIN ASHTON
1968–
British technologist who first
used the phrase 'Internet of
Things' in 1999

30-SECOND TEXT
Niamh Nic Daéid

*As big data grows
bigger, so do the
challenges of managing
and visualizing it.*

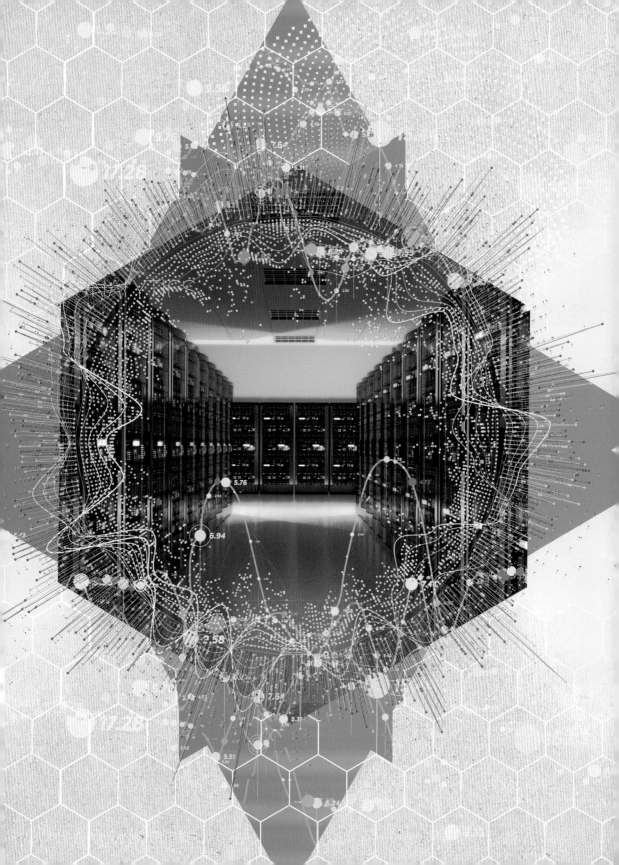

ARTIFICIAL INTELLIGENCE

the 30-second calculation

Primarily a feature of science

fiction where robots are talkative slaves fulfilling the needs of their human owners, artificial intelligence (AI) is portrayed as being able to have human-like high level functions. This form of AI – the point at which a computer is deemed to be sentient – is referred to as 'true' AI. It is open to debate how far from true AI we are, partly down to how it is defined, but research in this area is accelerating, as is the computational power available to it. Currently, AI mostly refers to 'deep learning' where complex, multilayered, learning algorithms feed results between the many tens to hundreds of layers in an optimized manner to dissect the input data into useful, human interpretable features. These multilayered architectures are mostly impenetrable and uninterpretable, leading to their often being termed 'black boxes'. Computer vision is one of the largest areas using this methodology to extract features from pictures or videos to better aid categorization and linking of photos or video footage. Examples are in autonomous vehicles or 'driverless cars', which scan the road to help them identify where to place the car, avoid obstructions and obey traffic signals. As with all machine learning methods, AI involves extensive training from large, known input datasets containing the features of interest.

3-SECOND COUNT
Artificial intelligence (AI) is the concept where computers become capable of performing mentally challenging tasks previously only possible by humans.

3-MINUTE TOTAL
The algorithms used in AI are extremely sensitive, and can end up learning underlying patterns which are intrinsic to the data but not explicitly described within it, leading to 'algorithmic bias'. An example of this occurred when an AI trained on the hiring practices of a large multinational company rejected female candidates because of historical gender inequalities in the industry.

RELATED TOPICS
See also
STATISTICS
page 38

PREDICTION
page 86

MACHINE LEARNING
page 132

3-SECOND BIOGRAPHY
ALAN TURING
1912–54
British mathematical genius who devised the Turing Test – a standard by which a computer could be called intelligent

30-SECOND TEXT
Christian Cole

Self-driving cars use artificial intelligence to interpret the world around them. They have learned to identify obstacles and to 'read' traffic signals or signs.

MACHINE LEARNING

the 30-second calculation

Typical computer programs

cannot do tasks that they were not programmed
to do. Machine learning methods are taught
specific tasks through performing functions
that optimize their success in completing the
tasks, just like human trial and error. Machine
learning can be supervised and unsupervised.
In supervised learning the algorithm is provided
categorical data and it tries to optimize the
distinction between the categories. A typical
example is an email spam filter which decides
whether email is 'spam' or 'not spam' based on
knowledge gained from the user marking certain
emails as spam. Supervised learning methods
require a computationally expensive training
stage where the algorithm is given a large set of
labelled examples, and it iteratively learns the
features of the dataset until it stops improving.
The learned algorithm is then provided with
new, unlabelled examples and is tested to see
how well it can predict the labels of the new
examples. This is then its calculated accuracy.
Unsupervised learning algorithms classify data
without the use of human-defined labels. The
methods usually cluster data into subsets
sharing similar features. Typically this is done by
abstracting the data and minimizing/maximizing
the differences between adjacent elements.
These methods are able to identify patterns
in the data and help reduce its complexity.

3-SECOND BIOGRAPHY
ARTHUR LEE SAMUEL
1901–90
American computing pioneer
who coined the term 'machine
learning' in 1959

30-SECOND TEXT
Christian Cole

*Machine learning is all
around us in the digital
world, performing
many mundane but
useful tasks such as
blocking spam emails.*

DATA VISUALIZATION

the 30-second calculation

Visually representing data is a complex dialogue between the presenter and the observer. Choices made by the presenter can have a very strong influence on how the information is understood by the observer. Likewise, human perception means different ways of presenting the same data can make it easier or harder to interpret. A good data visualization is one where understanding is intuitive to the untrained observer and allows them to make further deductions from the data. It uses visual communication theories as a foundation to bring out the best of the data. In the era of big data and artificial intelligence, data visualization has become increasingly useful and important in order to aid the interpretation of complex datasets. Particularly as data visualization can be automated via computer programs and presented in applications for user exploration. Many advances are being made to make good data visualization available within common programming languages such as Python and R. There are several rules and best practices for making good visualizations. The colours and shapes used can transform a boring figure into something impactful. 'Less is more' is a good mantra. Edward Tufte's data-ink ratio rule is a great guide; ink that does not convey data should be removed.

3-SECOND COUNT
Data visualization is a technical domain that combines visual communication theory, data science and graphic art; it is more than just plotting graphs.

3-MINUTE TOTAL
Data journalism is a large growth area for media organizations as their audiences become more demanding for clear analyses of complex topics. For example, election night visuals on TV and online have been transformed in recent years, driven in part by specialist websites.

RELATED TOPICS
See also
BIG DATA
page 128

USING SHAPE & COLOUR
page 136

COMPARING NUMBERS
page 138

3-SECOND BIOGRAPHY
EDWARD ROLF TUFTE
1942–
American statistician and author of *The Visual Display of Quantitative Information*. Credited with developing the 'data-ink ratio' term

30-SECOND TEXT
Christian Cole

Data visualization has a rich history in representing complex information in ways that are attractive and understandable.

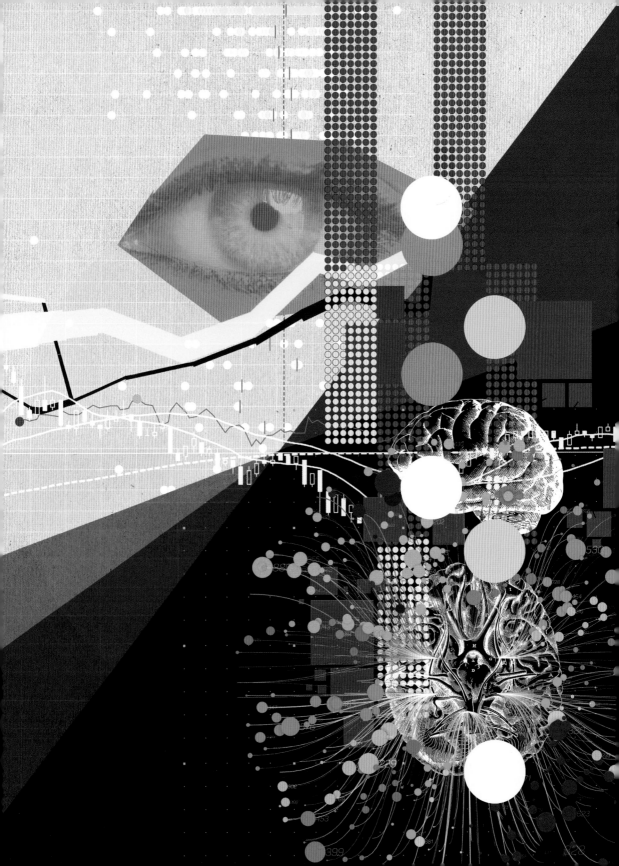

USING SHAPE & COLOUR

the 30-second calculation

Presenting quantitative data

in ways that are interesting, intuitive and meaningful is not as easy as it looks. As anyone who has had their brain tortured by optical illusions can attest, a person's perception can be fooled into seeing something that is not there. In comes visual communication theories (VCT): a collection of neuro-psychological observations that try to explain how the brain perceives what it sees. These laws govern how best to represent information by taking into account intrinsic knowledge of shape and colour. The Gestalt (unified whole) laws, developed in the early 1900s by Max Wertheimer, are based around how the mind tries to group objects together as best as possible in order to create structure within what is observed. The groupings occur in several ways: similarity (objects of similar shape or colour are related); continuation (the eye will follow a curve or line); closure (despite an object not being fully complete, if enough of it is drawn it will be perceived as a whole); proximity (objects close together are more related than those far apart); and figure and ground (the perception of there being a foreground distinct from a background). With these rules and theories a designer or data scientist can make intuitively meaningful visualizations of data. It is equally possible to use this knowledge to intentionally confuse and mislead an observer.

RELATED TOPIC
See also
DATA VISUALIZATION
page 134

3-SECOND BIOGRAPHY
MAX WERTHEIMER
1880–1943
Born in Austro-Hungarian Prague (now Czech Republic), Wertheimer was a psychologist who developed – together with colleagues Wolfgang Köhler and Kurt Koffka – the phi phenomenon into Gestalt psychology

30-SECOND TEXT
Christian Cole

3-SECOND COUNT
Visual theory dictates how humans perceive objects and colours; when visualizing or presenting information, shape and colour help the viewer to interpret the data correctly.

3-MINUTE TOTAL
Through evolution our eyes have adapted to respond to different wavelengths of light differently, hence we see in colour. People with normal colour perception are most sensitive to the green part of the visible light spectrum. However, 'colour blind' people have different colour sensitivities and colours in visualizations need to be chosen carefully so that everyone can see them. Most software packages have colour palettes that are suitable for this or there are online tools which can help.

Can you see a triangle in front of three white circles? Choice of shape and colour can lead the eye to see patterns and aid understanding.

COMPARING NUMBERS

the 30-second calculation

3-SECOND COUNT
Comparing numbers is something we do intuitively all the time as humans ('Does my sister have more sweets than me?'), but doing it meaningfully is hard.

3-MINUTE TOTAL
Context is important when comparing numbers, but can be lost if a number represents a summary statistic like an average. For example, 51 is the mean of both ranges 49, 50, 54 and 2, 4, 147, yet the two ranges would not be considered similar and nor should the means. Next time someone quotes numbers at you, make sure to ask them for the details.

When comparing two or more numbers we normally determine the absolute differences. So for the numbers 51, 200 and 36 it is clear that 200 is the biggest and 36 is the smallest, right? Well, it depends. Absolute numbers can hide a lot of things that humans do not like to think about, such as uncertainty, error, range or precision. The number 51 can be represented in several different ways: 51.04, 51 +/− 3 or 50, all of which have more or less the same meaning but imply something about the source of the information. The first implies the number was measured with high precision, the second that there is some uncertainty in the measurement and the third that the second digit is probably not reliable. When comparing numbers it is important to think about what the numbers represent and what units the numbers are quoted in: 51 milligrams vs 200 grams vs 36 kilograms, 36kg is the largest weight. Or for 51 car accidents in Dundee vs 200 in Birmingham vs 36 in Swansea, there are four times more accidents in Birmingham than Dundee, but Birmingham is seven times larger. This suggests there are more accidents per capita in Dundee than Birmingham. Before being able to compare numbers meaningfully, their provenance, measurement error, precision, units and whether they are summary statistics must be presented as well.

RELATED TOPICS
See also
STATISTICAL TESTS
page 58

MEAN
page 60

STANDARD DEVIATION
page 62

DATA VISUALIZATION
page 134

30-SECOND TEXT
Christian Cole

Numbers are used to represent many things from weights and scale to car crashes. Knowing what they mean allows us to make valid comparisons and informed decisions.

TRENDS

the 30-second calculation

One of the questions that we

most commonly want to ask when faced with
statistical data is: what is the underlying pattern
(if any)? Trends indicate some tendency for the
value of one variable to influence the value of
another. Any trend found can then be used to
understand the behaviour of the system being
measured. A positive trend (or positive
correlation) between two variables indicates
that, at least on average, as one variable
increases so does the other. An example could
be the weight of a bunch of bananas increasing
as the number of bananas in a bunch increases.
For a negative trend (or negative correlation),
if one variable gets bigger then the other tends
to get smaller. To determine the existence of
a trend between two variables, we often make
a 'scatter plot' of the data/measurements. This
is done by drawing a graph in which the values
of the two variables are along the two axes.
Points are then plotted on the graph to represent
the pairs of data values (in the above example,
the number of bananas and the weight of the
bunch). We then look for a line that fits the data
best in some way – sometimes called a 'trend
line' – for example, using linear regression.
Various statistical tests exist for determining
the strength and statistical significance of such
trends. In the business world, seeking these
trends is known as 'trend analysis'.

RELATED TOPIC
See also
LINEAR REGRESSION &
CORRELATION
page 76

3-SECOND BIOGRAPHIES
ADRIEN-MARIE LEGENDRE
& CARL FRIEDRICH GAUSS
1752–1833 & 1777–1855
French and German
mathematicians who pioneered
the least squares method of
seeking trends in data

30-SECOND TEXT
David Pontin

3-SECOND COUNT
Trends are patterns in
statistical data that
indicate some relationship
between two (or more)
quantities. They can be
obtained by visualizing
(plotting) the data or by
applying statistical tests.

3-MINUTE TOTAL
Determining trends in
measurements is important
in a wide range of areas,
from predicting future
market behaviour in
economics to assessing the
effectiveness of treatment
strategies in medicine.
These trends can be
positive or negative, can
be visualized graphically
and can be tested for using
a variety of different
statistical methods.

*There is a positive trend
between the number of
bananas in a bunch and
the weight of the bunch*

6 November 1869
Born in Bristol, England

1879
Studies at Christ's Hospital, London, where he distinguishes himself in classics and mathematics

1888
Studies mathematics at Trinity College, Cambridge

1892
Awarded the Cobden Prize for his essay 'A short account of England's foreign trade in the nineteenth century'

1895
Starts lecturing (part-time) in statistics at the newly founded London School of Economics (LSE)

1900
Appointed mathematics lecturer at Reading College (now Reading University), where he teaches until 1913 (in parallel with teaching at LSE)

1901
Publishes *Elements of Statistics*

1908
Appointed (part-time) reader in Statistics at LSE

1910
Publishes *An Elementary Manual of Statistics*

1913
Publishes *A General Course of Pure Mathematics*

1915
Appointed (part-time) professor at LSE

1919
Named the first incumbent of the Chair of Statistics at the University of London (which was held at LSE)

1922
Made a fellow of the British Academy

1924
Publishes *The Mathematical Groundwork of Economics*

1937
Appointed Commander of the British Empire

1940
Appointed acting director of the Oxford University Institute of Statistics

1950
Knighted

21 January 1957
Dies in Surrey, England

SIR ARTHUR LYON BOWLEY

Arthur Bowley was born in 1869 in Bristol and was raised by his mother (his father, a vicar in the Church of England, died in 1870). Between 1879 and 1888 he was educated at Christ's Hospital, London, where he won annual prizes in classics and mathematics. He went on to study mathematics at Trinity College, Cambridge, having been awarded a scholarship.

Bowley's interest in social conditions directed him towards the new field of statistics. At Cambridge, he studied for a short time with the economist Alfred Marshall, who influenced his career in economic statistics. For his essay 'A short account of England's foreign trade in the nineteenth century', Bowley received the Cobden Prize in 1892 (the study was published as a book in 1893). This prize was followed in 1895 by the Adam Smith Prize for his essay on changes in workers' wages presented to the Royal Statistical Society, which further led to the Guy Medal in Silver (he received the Guy Medal in Gold in 1935). He also began lecturing part-time at the London School of Economics when it opened in 1895.

In 1901 Bowley published *Elements of Statistics*. This book, which was based on the lectures he gave at the London School of Economics, is considered to be the first statistics textbook in the English language. Chapter VII consists of a lengthy exposition of 'The Graphic Method', which, in Bowley's opinion, is one of 'the two main methods of elementary statistics' (the other being the method of averages). As explained by Bowley, 'the chief use of diagrams is to afford a rapid view of the relation between two series of events' and 'also to present large groups of figures so that they shall be intelligible in their entirety'. This textbook was followed in 1910 by *The Elementary Manual of Statistics*.

For his work in economic statistics as well as social statistics (where he pioneered the use of sampling techniques for social surveys), Bowley received many honours: in 1893 he was elected fellow of the Royal Economic Society, in 1922 he was appointed fellow of the British Academy, in 1937 he was appointed a Commander of the British Empire, and in 1950 he was knighted.

Raluca Eftimie

RANGES

the 30-second calculation

3-SECOND COUNT
The range of a dataset describes the spread of the data and is defined as the difference between the highest and lowest observed values in the set.

3-MINUTE TOTAL
The range is used to obtain a basic understanding on the spread of various data points: from the student grades in a test (where the lowest/highest grades are important to identify weakest/strongest students in the class), to employees' salaries in a company (where lowest/highest salaries should match employees' skills and performance).

In statistics, the range of a dataset is a measure of the spread of this data. As the range uses only two values (the smallest and the largest data values), it cannot be used as the only measure of quantifying the spread, since it ignores a large amount of information associated with the data, such as the presence of outliers (observation values distant from all other observations, which can affect the values of the range). To address these limitations, other common measures of data spread are used in combination with the range: the standard deviation, the variance and the quartiles. The range of a dataset can be used to obtain a quick but rough approximation for the standard deviation. To approximate the standard deviation (σ) one can apply the so-called 'range rule', which states that the standard deviation of a dataset is approximately one fourth of the range of the data. The applicability of this 'range rule' is associated with the normal distributions, which can describe a large variety of real-world data and which ensure that 95% of the data is within two standard deviations (lower or higher) from the mean. Therefore, most of the data can be distributed over an interval that has the length of four standard deviations. Even if not all data is normally distributed, it is usually well behaved so that the majority falls within two standard deviations of the mean.

RELATED TOPICS
See also
NORMAL DISTRIBUTION
page 48

MEAN
page 60

STANDARD DEVIATION
page 62

QUARTILES
page 146

3-SECOND BIOGRAPHY
JOSEPH PRIESTLEY
1733–1804
English theologian and scientist who was one of the first to visualize historical data. In his *Chart of Biography* (which included 2,000 names between 1200 BCE and 1750 CE) he used horizontal lines to describe the lifespan of various individuals

30-SECOND TEXT
Raluca Eftimie

The range of a dataset is given as the difference between the smallest and largest values in the dataset.

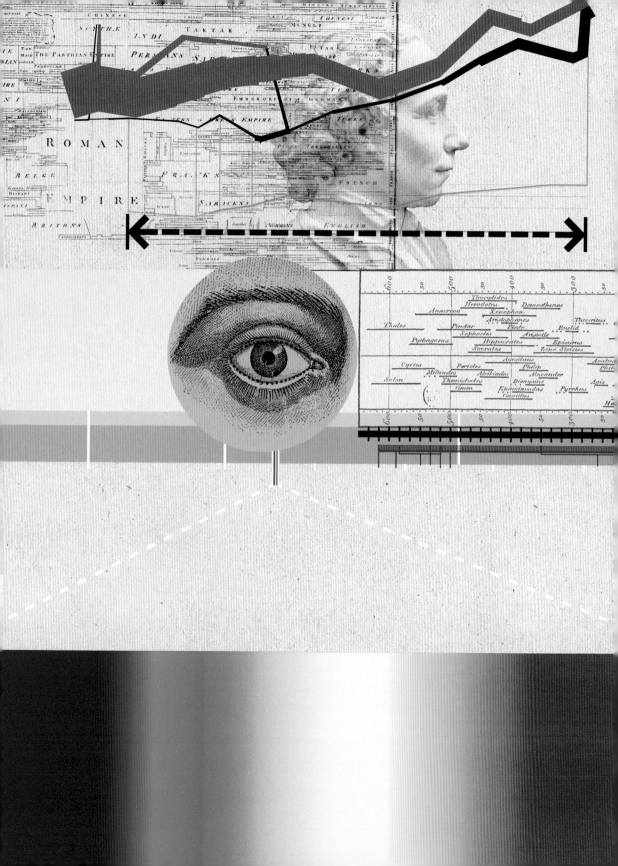

QUARTILES

the 30-second calculation

In statistics, the quartiles are

values that divide an (ordered) observation dataset into four subintervals on the number line. These four subintervals contain the following data: (1) the lowest 25% of data; (2) the second lowest 25% of data (until the median value); (3) the second highest 25% of data (just above the median); (4) the highest 25% of data. The three points that separate these four subintervals are the quartiles: Q1, the lower quartile, is the point between subintervals (1) and (2); Q2, the second quartile, is the point between subintervals (2) and (3); Q3, the upper quartile, is the point between subintervals (3) and (4). These quartiles tell us what numbers are higher than a certain percentage of the rest of the dataset. The quartiles are one of the statistical measures that describe the spread of a dataset (in addition to the range, variance and standard deviation). However, unlike other measures, they also tell us something about the centre of the data (as given by the median Q3). The spread of data can also be characterized by the interquartile range (IQR), which is the difference between the 3rd and 1st quartile: $IQR = Q3 - Q1$. The IQR can be used to calculate the outliers, those extreme values at the low and/or high ends of the dataset.

RELATED TOPICS
See also
STANDARD DEVIATION
page 62

RANGES
page 144

3-SECOND BIOGRAPHY
SIR ARTHUR LYON BOWLEY
1869–1957
British statistician who in 1901 published *Elements of Statistics*, which included graphical methods for finding the median and the quartiles

30-SECOND TEXT
Raluca Eftimie

3-SECOND COUNT
Quartiles are cut points that divide the range of a probability distribution or the observations in a sample into four groups of approximately equal sizes.

3-MINUTE TOTAL
Quartiles are useful because they offer information about the centre of the data, as well as its spread. For example, they can be used to obtain a quick understanding of students' grades in a test (where the lower 25% of students might fail the test, while the upper 25% of the students might obtain bonus points).

The three quartiles divide any given dataset into four sub-intervals.

APPENDICES

RESOURCES

BOOKS AND ARTICLES

For studying
Elementary Statistics
Robert R. Johnson and Patricia J. Kuby
(Cengage Learning, 2011)

*Fundamentals of Data Visualization:
A Primer on Making Informative and
Compelling Figures*
Claus Wilke
(O'Reilly Media, 2019)
The complete text of the book is also
available via an open licence at
serialmentor.com/dataviz

An Introduction to the Bootstrap
Bradley Efron and R. J. Tibshirani
(Chapman & Hall, 1993)

*An Introduction to Error Analysis: The Study
of Uncertainties in Physical Measurements*
John Robert Taylor
(University Science Books, 1999)

The Practice of Statistics (2nd Ed.)
Daniel S. Yates, David S. Moore and
Daren S. Starnes
(W. H. Freeman & Company, 2003)

Statistics for Dummies (2nd Ed.)
Deborah J. Rumsey
(For Dummies, 2016)

Statistics: From Data to Decision
Ann E. Watkins, Richard L. Scheaffer and
George W. Cobb
(Wiley, 2009)

*Statistics in the Real World: A Book of
Examples*
Donna Fox Stroup and Richard J. Larsen
(Macmillan, 1976)

'What is Bayesian Statistics?'
Sean R Eddy
Nature Biotechnology 22, September 2004
(https://www.nature.com/articles/nbt0904-
1177)

Popular science

The Art of Statistics: Learning from Data
David Spiegelhalter
(Pelican Books, 2019)
A wonderful book that makes statistics accessible to everyone.

Fermat's Last Theorem
Simon Singh
(Fourth Estate, 1997)
A historical novel about how a frustratingly simple comment in a book's margin drove a 350-year search for a solution.

Hello World: How to be Human in the Age of the Machine
Hannah Fry
(Transworld, 2018)
A modern look at how humans are influenced and affected by mathematical algorithms in everyday life.

How Not to be Wrong: The Hidden Maths of Everyday Life
Jordan Eilenberg
(Penguin, 2015)
An exploration of how mathematics reaches into all of our lives.

How to Lie with Statistics
Darrell Huff
(Penguin, 1991)
A great introduction to many of the concepts of statistics, presented in an accessible way.

Humble Pi: A Comedy of Maths Errors
Matt Parker
(Allen Lane, 2019)
The author presents real world problems caused by misunderstandings of maths and uses maths to explain some very public failures.

The Indisputable Existence of Santa Claus
Hannah Fry
(Transworld, 2017)
This fun, Christmas-themed book shows how maths can be useful even in the holidays!

Mathematics of Life: Unlocking the Secrets of Existence
Ian Stewart
(Profile Books, 2011)
An engaging view into what can be achieved when mathematicians and biologists work together to answer questions about living things.

RESOURCES continued

The Music of the Primes
Marcus du Sautoy
(Fourth Estate, 2003)
An exploration of one of the most
important unsolved problems in
mathematics and how it affects
almost everything that we do.

Zero: The Biography of a Dangerous Idea
Charles Seife
(Penguin Books, 2000)
The history of the number zero, a number
we take for granted, but one that did not
always exist. Its introduction was not
simple nor universally accepted.

ONLINE RESOURCES

'A brief history of numerical systems'
A great video explaining the history of
our modern numerical system.
ed.ted.com/lessons/a-brief-history-of-
numerical-systems-alessandra-king

'Alan Turing: Creator of modern computing'
An interactive website with a history of the
mathematician and code breaker Alan Turing.
www.bbc.com/timelines/z8bgr82#z3pnsbk

Archimedes lab
A website with learning topics on numeracy
together with puzzles and games for young
and old.
www.archimedes-lab.org

Information is Beautiful
A continuously updated highlight of the web's
best data visualizations. Has an annual award
to showcase the best of the year.
informationisbeautiful.net

MacTutor History of Mathematics Archive
The go-to online resource for the history
of mathematics.
www-history.mcs.st-andrews.ac.uk/index.
html

Medium
Blog site of the influential data scientist
Elijah Meeks. Lots of useful information
and engaging visualizations to learn from.
https://medium.com/@Elijah_Meeks

Wolfram Alpha
You can find definitions of mathematical
meanings and perform mathematical
calculations including solving algebraic
equations.
www.wolframalpha.com

ONLINE LEARNING

Mathematics and Statistics on the Open
University
www.openuniversity.edu/courses/find/
mathematics-and-statistics

Data Science courses on Coursera
www.coursera.org/browse/data-science

Mathematics course list on EdX
www.edx.org/course/subject/math

NOTES ON CONTRIBUTORS

CONSULTANT EDITORS

Niamh Nic Daéid is the Director of the Leverhulme Research Centre for Forensic Science, University of Dundee. She is a Fellow of the Royal Society of Edinburgh and holds fellowships of five other national societies including the Royal Statistical Society. She has an honours degree in Chemistry and Mathematics from Trinity College, Dublin and the Dublin Institute of Technology, where she specialised in statistics. She completed her PhD in Chemistry at the Royal College of Surgeons in Ireland and also holds a degree in Psychology. Niamh has published widely in the forensic science literature, pioneering the use of chemometric analysis in the interpretation of complex data sets relating to forensic science research.

Christian Cole is a Data Scientist and Principal Investigator at the Leverhulme Research Centre for Forensic Science, University of Dundee. He has a degree and PhD in Chemistry, but his recent focus has been on biological problems with large datasets, using statistical methods to analyse multi-faceted biological data. Chris has published more than 35 peer-reviewed publications.

CONTRIBUTORS

Raluca Eftimie is Reader in Mathematics at the University of Dundee. She obtained a PhD in Applied Mathematics from the University of Alberta, Canada. She is interested in various applications of mathematics to ecology, epidemiology, cell biology and immunology, and is the author of *Hyperbolic and Kinetic Models for Self-organised Biological Aggregations: A Modelling and Pattern Formation Approach* (Springer, 2019).

Harry Gray is the David and Claudia Harding Foundation Fellow in Communicating Statistics, Risk, and Uncertainty in Forensic Science at the Leverhulme Research Centre for Forensic Science at the University of Dundee. His research targets the barriers in understanding quantitative forensic evidence presented in the courtroom, so that it may be communicated, examined, and evaluated effectively. He completed his PhD in Mathematical Genomics and Medicine at the University of Cambridge, researching ways to accurately estimate correlations between molecular quantities with small sample sizes.

Joyce Kafui Klu is a Post-Doctoral Research Statistician at the Leverhulme Centre for Forensic Science, University of Dundee. After completing her PHD in Statistics from the University of Oxford, Joyce started her career as a Medical Statistician at the University of Oxford and Research Assistant in Data Science at the University of Reading. Joyce's current research is into the statistical analysis of forensic evidence.

John McDermott is a lecturer in mathematics at the University of Dundee and has taught mathematics at universities in Ireland, England and Scotland for more than 25 years. He is interested in aspects of discrete mathematics, including computational group theory and cryptography. His main focus is on mathematics education – and particularly on the challenges around the teaching and learning of mathematics in higher education.

David Pontin obtained his PhD from the University of St Andrews and took up a postdoctoral position at the University of Waikato, New Zealand before moving to a Research Scientist position in the Space Science Centre at the University of New Hampshire, USA. He is currently a mathematics lecturer at the University of Dundee, Scotland, and holds a Personal Chair in Fluid and Plasma Modelling. David's research is focussed around mathematical and computational modelling of fluids and plasmas. Particular applications of his work include modelling explosive energy release in astrophysical plasmas including the sun's atmosphere, and in 2011 he was awarded a Philip Leverhulme Prize for Astronomy and Astrophysics.

INDEX

A

absolute risk 98, 100
al-Khwarizmi, Muhammad
  ibn Musa 116
algorithmic bias 126, 130
algorithms 80, 86, 116, 126
  genetic algorithms 126
  learning algorithms
    127, 132
alternating current 22
alternative hypothesis
  58, 88
American Statistical
  Association 66
ANOVA test 56, 58
Arbuthnot, John 58
arithmetic mean 60
artificial intelligence
  (AI) 116, 130
artificial neural
  networks 126
Ashton, Kevin 128
autonomous vehicles 130
average
  see mean
Avogadro's number 12, 14

B

base 106, 108
Bayes' Theorem 90, 93
Bayes, Thomas 90, 92–3
Bayesian networks 126
Bayesian probability
  82, 90
bell curve 36, 48
Bernoulli, Jacob 112
Bhaskara II 28

bias
  algorithmic 126, 130
  numerical 102
big data 128
binary 106, 108
binary digits (bits) 12, 24
binary number 24, 108
binomial distribution
  36, 46, 51
Blackstone, Sir William
  88
bootstrapping 72
Bowley, Sir Arthur Lyon
  142–3, 146
Bradley, James 60
bus timetables 102

C

calculus 28, 85, 110
  differential calculus 85
cancer 96, 100
Cantor, Georg 26
Cardano, Gerolamo 22,
  32–3, 52, 82
case-control studies 66
causal relationship 86
census 36, 40
Central Limit Theorem 48
Chi-square distribution
  36, 46, 56, 58
Chuprov, Alexander
  Ivanovich 40
cicadas 20
cluster sampling 42
clusters 36, 42, 132
Cochran, William
  Gemmell 64

coin tossing 52, 82, 90
colour 134, 136
combinations 120
common denominator
  114
comparing numbers 138
complex conjugate 22
complex numbers
  22, 48, 51
composite number 12, 20
conditional probability 94
confidence interval 62,
  70, 72
confidence level 88
conjugate 12
  complex conjugate 22
constants 14, 51
continuous distributions
  46
continuous numbers 26
continuous random
  variables 52
correlation 76, 140
counting 108
critical value 80, 88
cryptography 12, 20

D

data journalism 134
data visualization 126, 134
data-ink ratio 126
de Moivre, Abraham 48,
  50–1, 82, 93
de Moivre's formula 48, 51
decimal point 110
decimals 26, 112
decision tree 126

Dedekind, Richard 18
deep learning 126, 130
degrees of belief 90
del Ferro, Scipione 33
denominator 12, 106, 114
dependent variables 44, 76
Descartes, René 14, 22
diagnostic testing 96, 118
dice 33, 52, 94
  see also games of
    chance
differential calculus 85
dimensionality reduction
  126
Diophantus of Alexandria
  123
discrete distributions 46
discrete numbers 20, 24,
  52
discrete random variables
  52
distance, measurement
  of 26
distribution
  binomial 36, 46, 51
  Chi-square 36, 46, 56,
    58
  continuous 46
  discrete 46
  exponential 46
  Gaussian 36
  normal 46, 48, 51
  Poisson 36, 46
  probability 46, 48
  statistical 38, 46
  uniform 37, 46
driverless cars 130

INDEX

ACKNOWLEDGEMENTS

EDITORS' ACKNOWLEDGEMENTS
This has been a genuinely fun book to have the pleasure to be involved in. We are enormously grateful to the amazing team of authors who brought the text together at very short notice. We hope they are as delighted with the final result as we are and they should be enormously proud of their individual and collective achievements. Their writings have been magically and beautifully brought to life by the outstanding illustrations and exceptional talent of Steve Rawlings. Every book has a team that works with the authors and editors to make things happen. This book would never have come to fruition without the patience and quiet persuasiveness of Joanna Bentley, senior project editor at Ivy Press, and Jane Roe, our copy editor. We owe enormous gratitude also to the design and production teams who made the final book a reality and boy, did they make us look good!

PICTURE CREDITS
The publisher would like to thank the following for permission to reproduce copyright material on the following pages:

Alamy Stock Photo/ Heritage Image Partnership Ltd 50, Keystone Press 68, Pictorial Press Ltd 32, Science History Images 122.
European Southern Observatory 19.
Europeana Collections/ Finnish National Gallery 31; The European Library 19.
Library of Congress 19, 111.
Shutterstock/ Aaron Amat 109; Aaron HY Chen 17; Africa Studio 83; Aha-Soft 47; Aleksandar Mijatovic 135; Alexy Kljatov 67; Alexyz3d 117; all_is_magic 87; Alted Studio 83; Andrey_Popov 6; Andy Dean Photography 15; AnEduard 71; Anton_Ivanov 6; Antonio Gravante 115; Aperture75 67; Aphelleon 67, 117; Arcady 87; arka38 45; Ayse Pemra Yuce 43; Bedrin 95; Bikeworldtravel 113; Bildagentur Zoonar GmbH 103; Billion Photos 15; Bjorn Heller 99; Bruce Rolff 87, 131; Chjusman 121; cla78 139; Claudio Divizia 103; creative_design_2017 99; Cynthia Farmer 59; Dan Kosmayer 53; Daniela Pelazza 71; DariaRen 115; Dario Lo Presti 67; dashadima 15; Davydenko Yuliia 89; dencg 53; Denys Prykhodov 8; Dimitris Leonidas 15; DivinHX 131; Dogholiday 89; doomu 71, 109; Dreamcreation 73, 135; eAlisa 49; ekkapon 17; Elena Schweitzer 45; Elena100 31; enterphoto 89; Evannovostro 117; exopixel 61; Flipser 115; Flyingv3 21; Fresh_Studio 119; Garumna 89; GarryKillian 129, 135; Georgios Kollidas 61; Giuseppe Donatiello 73; Good Shop Background 67; Green angel 103; GzP_Design 145; HomeStudio 25; horiyan 65; HPLTW 113; ibrandify gallery 89; ichadsgn 71; icolourful 17; ifong 17, 45; imagewriter 137; Ink Drop 139; itechno 17; iunewind 15, 61; Iurii Stepanov 109; Ivan Alex Burchak 119; Jacek Chabraszewski 97; Kai Celvin 117; KKulikov 27; Konstantin L 27; Kotin 89; KRAHOVNET 41; Kyryloff 27; Luria 91; locote 45; Lurii Stepamov 25; M. Unal Ozmen67; Macrovector 67; Makhh 63; Makhnack_S 29; Marso 141; martan 53; Matee Nuserm 139; Matt Benoit 25; mattesimages 83, 89; matthew25 97; Mauro Matacchione 27; Marzolino 84; mdbildes 111; melih2810 71; MicroOne 39; milart 141; Miloje 113; modustollens 113; montego 45, 95; Morphart Creation 145; Motionblur Studios 97; Mr. Rashad 21; musmellow 139; NadzeyaShanchuk 73; Nataliia Nata 97; Neamov 71; Nerthuz 15, 19; Nichca 7; Nikelser Kate 109; notbad 133; Oakozhan 87; Oleh Svetiukha 115; Oleksandr Panasovsky 115; Oleksiy Mark 129; Orn Rin 87; PaoloBruschi 133; Pavlo S 117; Peter Hermes Furian 145; phipatbig 117; Phonalamai Photo 117; photopixel 111; pikepicture 95; PixMarket 39; Rashevskyi Viacheslav 15; Robert Adrian Hilman 17; Robert Lucian Crusitu 109; Romanova Natali 131; Romariolen 45; Rost9 53; sansak 101; Sarah Holmlund 117; Savvapanf Photo 101; Sebastian Kaulitzki 119, 135; sebra 61; Seregam 61; Sergey Chayko 83; ShadeDesign 117; shahreen 47; sirtavelalot 41; Social Media Hub 89, 101; Sorbis 113; SP-Photo 45; stocker1970 45; Stu Shaw 29; Tatiana Shpeleva 43, 131; temp-64GTX 129; This Is Me 53; Thomas Pajot 147; TotemArt115; Trodler 15; Trong Nguyen 103; TwinkleStudio 25; Valex 133; Vector.design 117; vesna cvorovic 95; Vidual Generation 74; Vikpit 131; Vladystock 131, 133; VOLYK IEVGENII 29; whiteMocca 63; Whitevector 103; WhiteWings 25; WorldWide 103; Yes – Royalty Free 31, 67, 95, 97; Yevgenij_D 139; Zakharevych Vladyslav 119; Zentilla 121.
Smithsonian Libraries 141.
Stella Bowen (painting owned by the London School of Economics an Political Science) 142.
Wellcome Library, London 25, 39, 49, 61, 65, 77, 111, 135.
Wikimedia Commons/07bargem 135; A1E6 47; Adrignola 25; AlexNett22 133; Boivie/Maksim 37; Booya 137; cmglee 39; Cyc 133 Daderot 115, 145; DkEgy 134, 145; Ellasdabbas 135; EpochFail 141 Heds 1 49, 63; HiTe 63, 73; IkamusumeFan 59, 74; IllestFlip 111; Ilya Voyager 19; Jhedengren 133; Jjbeard 25; Johannes Ganz 19; Joseph Priestley 145; Kmf164 135; Lalala666 39; Martin Grandjean 135; Mehmet Atif Ergun 145; Mikael Häggström 97; Muhali 77; NASA 19, 49; Pearson Scott Foresman 49; Risani 109; Sigbert 77; Slashme 21; Trlkly 23; Twisp 111; Hermann Dietler 39; Wolfkeeper 25.

All reasonable efforts have been made to trace copyright holders and to obtain their permission for the use of copyright material. The publisher apologizes for any errors or omissions in the list above and will gratefully incorporate any corrections in future reprints if notified